Wake-Up Shake-Up

THRIVE!

How to Lift Up Your Life in Your 50's and Beyond

— Swiss secrets to not growing old —

Ellen Kocher & Dominique Ben Dhaou

PAUL SMITH PUBLISHING
London

Published by Paul Smith Publishing London 2021

A CIP catalogue record for this title is available from the British Library

ISBN PB 978 1 912597 18 5

ISBN eBook 978 1 912597 19 2

Paul Smith Publishing

www.paulsmithpublishing.co.uk

To our families who gave us wings to fly

Contents

Introduction

"There is a fountain of youth: it is your mind, your talents, the creativity you bring to your life and the lives of people you love. When you learn to tap this source, you will truly have defeated age." Sophia Loren

You've grabbed this book because you don't want to *grow* old. Not to be confused with getting older, which no one can avoid, not *growing* old is about feeling youthful, energetic and vibrant rather than grumpy, worn out and uncool. It's about purposeful living and a determination to live life to its fullest, beginning right now.

Wake-Up, Shake-Up, Thrive! is a unique wake-up call designed to inspire the 50+ generation to grasp the modern ageing paradigm before it's too late, to shake-up mindsets and attitudes to embrace the years ahead and to offer vision, tools, tips and guidelines to thrive now.

This book is written for the 50+ generation — yet its principles are ageless and timeless. We've noticed that at around 50, people get an itch to do things differently: go beyond their dreams, be unique, make a difference and elevate their lives.

Wake-Up, Shake-Up, Thrive! is based on our personal success stories after 50, backed by decades of experience living, working and thriving in Switzerland and overseas. For over 20 years we've researched best practices, tested and streamlined new approaches to create this simple and exclusive book to gear up for the many years of vibrant and meaningful life ahead.

Elevating this once-in-a-lifetime transition requires an approach that incorporates multiple Dimensions of well-being because they intricately affect each other. Think of retirement years, for example. Can a financial situation affect health and vice versa? Might our emotional state affect how we feel physically? Like the Gears of a Swiss watch, we need to calibrate each Gear individually, so they turn harmoniously together. Understanding, revising and balancing these Gears wisely is essential because when one Gear turns, the others move too.

We've separated our human timepiece into five meaningful *Gears*: Physical, Emotional, Intellectual, Spiritual and Financial. This book will reveal how to calibrate each Gear and to integrate them, so you can take full charge of life and run it with the precision of a Swiss watch.

Swiss watches are known for their refinement, accuracy and eternal beauty. Switzerland, our homeland to such timepieces, along with banking secrecy and snowy alps, is consistently ranked as one of the happiest places with the longest life expectancy in the world. All this, while consuming more chocolate than any other nation! This is only the beginning of the *Swiss Touch* our book explores to elevate your life.

Green Thumbs — a symbol of our ecological concern for global sustainability — will also nudge themselves throughout the book to enhance your awareness, understanding and skill-power, because we believe that sustainability is not only at the core of maintaining our planet, but at the heart of optimal ageing too.

For us, being *cool* means embracing our individuality in whatever we pursue. How we show up in the world and how we feel deep inside, from the clothing we choose to the attitude we have. *Coolness* is a result of how we view ourselves. It's being proud of who we are and not apologizing for differences or preferences. Regardless of time, *cool* will never go out of style. We believe that's the best way *not to grow old*. This book will help readers tap into their coolness in every Dimension and maybe, just maybe, develop a zest of *Swissness* and *Greenness* along the way.

Because timeless solutions require lasting change, the *Thrive-Guide*, at the end of the book, is designed to activate and elevate your journey at your pace. A personal coach to refer to anytime, anywhere.

Each of the Five Dimensions — Physical, Emotional, Intellectual, Spiritual and Financial — has a dedicated *Thrive-Guide* section and style. Readers will discover our top picks from years of workshops and coaching including tried and tested exercises, checklists, assessments, tips, and games designed to motivate and maintain momentum and progress.

Wake-Up, Shake-Up, Thrive! is a complete everyday companion to put into action to shift from knowing what to do, to *actually doing it.* Whether for practical advice to save time and effort, or for the insight needed to make sound decisions about the future, it's time to wake-up, shake-up and thrive!

We've been inspired by famous seniors such as Tina Turner, octogenarian American-born rock star and actress, who has lived and thrived in Switzerland for over 20 years; Irma Dütsch, the first Swiss woman chef to be awarded a Michelin star, who pursued her career worldwide until past 80; and Des Hun Wang, the hot grandpa, who switched from acting to modelling and got on his first catwalk at 79. These are just some of the many examples, renowned or simply unknown, who chose to be cool at any age.

Now we want to inspire YOU, before you *grow old*.

1

The Story Behind
Wake-Up, Shake-Up, Thrive!

Ellen

I was born in 1962 in Hartford, Connecticut, USA. The second of three children, between two brothers. My mom always told me I came into the world at the speed of light, and I believe I've kept that speed ever since. Everything I do — walking, learning, even driving my car — happens fast. I claim it's to save time to appreciate the rest of life's pleasures!

Growing up by a lake, swimming, sailing, and walking to *Ofshay's* General Store made me into a true *small-town-girl*. I loved and excelled in school and chose to study Economics at a college in rural Vermont where the great outdoors, skiing and Vermonters further nurtured my small-town-girl self. My world grew bigger when I went to study in Rome, Italy, where I fell in love with Europe, its food, lifestyle and travel. That's when I discovered Switzerland.

After graduation, I returned to Europe to perfect my Italian and learn French. Quaint Switzerland seemed the perfect choice providing multiple languages and suiting my small-town-girl personality. Two years later I met and married my husband (my own *Swiss Touch*). For our first eight years we focused on our double income no kids career in the financial sector. We lived in Geneva and then New York City, where we had the opportunity to grow, discover and forge lasting relationships worldwide.

We left New York and settled back into a tiny village outside of Geneva — often joking we moved from a million people and practically no flies to a million flies and practically no people. It is here that we started our family. I balanced career and family life until our third child was born and then decided to become a full-time mom. I loved my new role, juggling three kids, renovating a house, cooking like a chef while running the entire family operation. Though things felt right, something unsettled me. I was about 20 kilos overweight, missed the self-confidence my career gave me and craved something more. I had never felt this way before.

One day — frustrated with my weight and lack self-esteem — I snuck out to join a weight loss program. I gradually lost 20 kilos, discovered the vibrant Swiss lifestyle I was craving and within a year had completely changed my way of eating, moving and living. Weight Watchers then offered me a job bringing weight management to the workplace; it was a perfect fit. For the next nine years I coached over 200 people weekly on how to manage their weight. However, I came to realize that a weight-loss program did not encourage lasting behavior change in other areas — such as sleep or stress — that strongly influence eating habits. Individuals and organizations needed an all-inclusive approach.

Conscious of the effect that a holistic, preventative approach to well-being has on critical issues such as stress, resilience and burnout, I decided to study and become a Health and Wellness Coach. I obtained certifications in Health Coaching, Mindful Eating, Workplace Wellness and most recently, at 56, a master's degree in Health and Wellness Coaching. *Wake-Up, Shake-Up, Thrive!* enables me to share my passion, expertise and personal experience so you can flourish today.

Dominique

I was born in February 1965 in Geneva, Switzerland. A first child long awaited by my parents, who had focused on building a business and career since their wedding day. My brother was born 18 months later.

We had a loving and happy childhood, though my dad was often busy working and we didn't see him much. Our parents took us travelling to exciting places full of unforgettable memories. I realize now that those years nurtured my curiosity and passion for travel as well as my desire to make the best of each moment.

As a teenager, all I dreamt of was travelling the world. The idea of becoming a flight attendant sounded fantastic, until my parents gently reminded me that I suffered from air sickness! Suddenly, I was at a loss as to how to fulfil my dream. One evening, during dinner with family friends, I heard about Lausanne's world-renowned Hotel School. That was it. I could explore the world working in fancy hotels. The only obstacle was the ten-year waiting list for this exclusive school.

So, at the ripe old age of eleven, I rushed to enroll at the Hotel School trusting the power of my lucky stars — and this trust paid off. A cancellation allowed me to enter at 18. Four years later, degree in hand, I started looking fanatically to move abroad, unsuccessfully for several years.

Fate finally landed me a job in a luxury hotel in Manhattan. Though those years were a tremendous challenge, working like a dog and struggling with little money, I loved every moment and will treasure them forever. Where else could I have met Madonna, Phil Collins and many other such cool hotel guests? It felt like a dream, yet it was my reality.

Returning to quiet, discrete Switzerland from hectic, bustling Manhattan was a shock. However, it turned out to be a great career opportunity working for Levi Strauss in Human Resources (HR). Over the next 30 years, I took on HR responsibilities for organizations ranging from 10 to 90,000 employees. I spent most of my time travelling — my thirst, enthusiasm, energy and passion to explore were the same as in my teens.

Marrying the man of my life in the middle of my career was a blessing I was longing for. It gave me the balance I needed to sustain the intense pace of my professional life.

Turning 50 made me realize there was a different way to work and live. I also realized I was exhausted and, most importantly, that my husband and I, as a couple, deserved more. Two life changing wake-up calls.

I decided it was time for a new beginning and 18 months later I left the organization and the team I loved with no other job to back me up. Quitting my job to rebalance my life at age 50 seemed a huge risk. It felt like jumping off a plane without a parachute, yet it proved to be the best decision ever. That free fall helped me truly find myself at 53.

Trusting my inner gut and knowledge, I decided to create a business to support people who feel their current career no longer fits. Despite financial worries and discouraging opinions from well-meaning people, my business quickly grew and expanded in over ten countries in less than a year.

Today, I understand that Switzerland provided the roots of my strength, my values and perseverance to go on, no matter what. Along with my years abroad, I now have real and practical insight to share with you so that you can outgrow your aspirations too.

It took me years to wake-up and shake-up, but it came at the perfect time. Where I am today is proof that it's never too late. *Wake-Up, Shake-Up, Thrive!* is at the heart of what I live.

Wake-Up, Shake-Up, Thrive!

Little did we know that a professional lunch meeting in Geneva would define our future. Over food and wine, our common passions were obvious — the love for our country, people, food and life. That day, we understood that by blending our experience and expertise along with everything we know and love about the Swiss mindset and lifestyle, we could make a greater impact on more people our age.

It's sometimes said that the Swiss *excel in mediocrity.* This might just be the coolest secret to well-being and optimal ageing. No extremes. No excesses. No perfection. No showing-off. Just a little ingenuity and common-sense balancing life for health and happiness. Swiss resourcefulness has allowed our country to become — with practically no natural resources — one of the wealthiest in the world. Our national mindset prioritizes human respect, quality and precision — like a good Swiss watch — shedding light on just a few of the greatest secrets to ageing well. We call it the *Swiss Touch.*

Most people come to us for support for one specific reason, yet our coaching ends up impacting multiple dimensions of their lives. For example, Deborah came to Ellen for weight loss and discovered that her overeating was due to job dissatisfaction and stress. Once Dominique helped her navigate her job stress, she lost weight effortlessly. Fred, on the other hand, hired Dominique to help him find a new job, but the real reason behind his failure to get hired was his lack of self-esteem and confidence to present himself at his best. Working with Ellen inspired him to skip the peanuts, get back on the treadmill, present himself with confidence and land a new job.

We realized that together we could provide the holistic, comprehensive, *Swiss Touch* our clients needed to thrive. Combining Dominique's expertise in creating purposeful professional lives, with Ellen's proficiency in supporting well-being through health and lifestyle, is the foundation of our approach. Together, we have elevated hundreds of lives and observed the real difference we can inspire by supporting amazing individuals over 50. This book is an extension of our passionate desire to create a sustainable ripple effect as far and long as possible.

We bring over 60 years of combined real experience alongside our Swiss mindset for success. Since their meeting, Dominique has motivated Ellen into doubling her income and Ellen has inspired Dominique into sleeping, eating and moving better resulting in 11 kilos less. Our proven tools, techniques and tips can transform your life, too.

"It's never too late to be what you might have become. Your third, long, phase of life is a phenomenal opportunity to pursue dreams and passions that you might have put on hold or not even known you had!" George Elliot

---

This book will help you build the strength, resilience and attitude you need to elevate your years beyond 50. It's meant to wake-up conversations and raise awareness about ageing. It intends to shake-up mindsets and behaviors while providing innovative solutions that inspire you to thrive.

Let's start by waking up!

Wake-Up!

Wake-up to Demographics

Almost one in ten people in the world is over sixty. This is estimated to double during your lifetime. The *silver tsunami* is upon us!

You started to age as soon as you turned 25. However, you determine *how* you age. According to the World Health Organization, how we age is only roughly related to our age in years. Lifestyle determines 70% of the characteristics we commonly associate with ageing such as slowing down, memory or frailty.

Today, more than ever, understanding the challenges, stakes, risks and opportunities of demographic trends is crucial to make appropriate life decisions.

What the above demographic facts mean is firstly, you can change how you age by choosing your lifestyle and secondly, you better act now because it's highly likely you have a long life ahead.

Wake-Up to Your Brain and Ageing

Research suggests that *crystalized intelligence,* the accumulation of knowledge, facts, and skills acquired during your life, increases through-out adulthood. Older adults are able to overcome many age-related challenges by tapping into their crystalized intelligence.

Rockefeller University found that the hippocampus, a region of the brain associated with memories, learning, and emotion, continues to create new cells, regardless of age. While older people might sometimes require more time to learn new things, they can understand and remember new material just as well as younger people.

Despite expressing health and money concerns, older generations tend to experience less stress than the younger ones. They are likely to be happier and less inclined to get angry, mostly because they manage their emotions better. You may be surprised to discover that people are generally revealed to be happier in their youth and then again after 70. Isn't that cool?

What's more, thanks to experience and wisdom, older people are better at reasoning through social dilemmas and conflicts. They understand all aspects of situations and come up with reasonable resolutions more spontaneously and easily.

Marriage tends to improve ageing. This is perhaps because long-time couples have more occasions to express affection, especially retirees and empty nesters. This holds true for each of our own couples; together, we tally up over 50 years of happy marriage.

Self-esteem tends to soar with age and increases with education, good health, and rewarding employment. However, around the age of 50, it takes a dip, often coinciding with that itch to seek a new sense of purpose or self. Sound familiar?

What this all means is that your brain is not declining, and you are not becoming irrelevant. You have every reason to embrace your new future, to be bold and to re-discover a true new purpose, now.

Wake-Up to Buying Power

According to Credit Suisse Bank, seniors are the fastest-growing consumer age group in the world. Boomers already account for 50 to 60% of consumer spending in developed markets with a rising share of income compared with other age groups. Yay!

Aged 50+ spending trends emphasize leisure through material goods such as fitness and outdoor gear, experiences such as excursions and travel and personal care, style and beauty. In the UK, for instance, women over 60 already account for a quarter of all beauty sales — more than double compared to a decade ago. We are also observing significant growth in 50+ men consumers for preventative self-care and natural ageing enhancements.

Therefore, your attitude toward spending really matters and you cannot ignore this when planning your future. Exploring and perhaps shifting your mindset about money can help you feel secure and confident about your financial future.

Wake-Up to Working

Did you know that people who work hard at a job they enjoy, live the longest? We have a projected lifespan of well over 80 years, so, depending upon when you retire — if you retire — that sums up to 20-30 years of exciting, active life to Gear-up for.

According to Deloitte, approximately 40% of all economically active 50 to 60-year-olds would like to work beyond retirement age and one-third of them would have continued to work given the opportunity.

Worldwide entrepreneurship activity for the same age group has doubled in the last decade and their startups are almost three times more likely to succeed than youth startups.

Today, workers aged 55+ make up nearly one-quarter of the total workforce in Europe and the United States. Each year, retirees account for a higher proportion of the global population, while too few younger workers enter the labor force to replace them. This skills deficit will be significant by 2030 creating both a huge gap and an opportunity.

So, there will be more work opportunities for our generation in the future. Today, the traditional retirement model known as freedom *from* work sounds more like freedom *to* work. Cool ageing means rethinking work agility, skills, objectives and collaborating with other generations in innovative ways.

Wake-Up to Switzerland

Switzerland has held the world's top place for life expectancy and happiness for decades and represents many ideals which lie at the very heart of our spirits.

Quality of life is the core and pride of Swiss culture. For instance, to preserve calm, it's illegal to be too noisy or shop on Sundays. Mandatory breaks are strictly enforced at work and school.

Switzerland consistently boasts the lowest rates of unemployment and poverty in Europe. Secure and stable foreign policies have positioned the country to be a global reference of peace for over 200 years. Thanks to its economic stability, excellent education and resourcefulness, our tiny nation is exemplary.

Happiness and well-being in Switzerland are not about striving for perfection, but about balance. The *Swiss Touch* is about adjusting and compromising to flourish from the inside out.

Let's be inspired by the Swiss!

Wake-Up Wrap-Up

"On a personal level, most of us would consider the possibility of living longer, more active, healthy lives as a fantastic opportunity. Translating this enthusiasm to the societal level fosters openings for innovative thinking on how we might create a future blessed with meaning, for all generations." Kristel Van der Elst

Some see life beyond fifty and, ultimately, retirement as a new world of opportunities. Others approach it with concern. Those who prepare and plan for this phase tend to appreciate it and thrive, while those who neglect it, often end up living with tension or regret. A purpose-driven plan aligned with your values, goals, culture and life circumstances is the best way to age well.

Until now, life followed a predictable pattern: study, work, retire, expire. Our wake-up call reveals an exciting emerging demographic reality which you cannot change. You can, however, change how you think about it and prepare for it. By embracing our multi-generation planet and the many cool opportunities illustrated throughout this book, you can turn disruptive demographics into productive possibilities for yourself and for all generations.

Your personal wake-up call needs to go far beyond financial planning; it must call upon every Dimension of your well-being in order to last.

Your Dimensions influence and impact each other directly. Therefore, though we explore each Dimension separately, it is essential to always consider them as a whole — *holistically*.

Similar to our Swiss watch, each Dimension of ageing is like a watch Gear demanding regular revision and lubrication to tick harmoniously. In turn, the whole watch needs regular winding and calibration to continue running smoothly. Through our Five-Dimensional approach, we provide what you need to craft your *personal timepiece* for a long, quality life.

How does visualizing your purposeful future — longer, easier, savvier — make you feel now?

2

Overview of The Five Dimensions of Well-Being

"The good life is a process, not a state of being. It is a direction not a destination." Carl Rogers

---

We've separated your personal timepiece into five meaningful Gears: Physical, Emotional, Intellectual, Spiritual and Financial. Understanding, revising and balancing your Gears wisely is essential because when you turn one Gear, the others move, too.

Like any journey, we need to start at the base, Gear-up and equip ourselves well. So, let's roll up our sleeves and start your ascent.

Your Basecamp

Multiple studies, research and experience confirm that today's top ageing fears are:

- Loss of independence
- Declining health
- Running out of money
- Inability to live at home
- Death of loved ones and loneliness.

Each of these worries is, in one way or another, linked to physical health; the basecamp of your *age-well journey*.

Lifestyle influences 70% of your physical ageing and therefore offers an enormous potential to improve your future. In the Physical Dimension, you will discover that Nutrition, Movement, Sleep and Mindfulness are the most impactful areas on longevity.

Your Emotional Essentials

After age 50, our bodies, careers and environments change remarkably, triggering a fountain of emotions. Research shows that more than 90% of our decisions are emotions-based, so, understanding and improving your emotional well-being is critical in making the right decisions for your future.

When Daniel Goleman's book *Emotional Intelligence (EI); Why It Can Matter More Than IQ* was published in 1985, it raised awareness and mainstream acceptance of the impact emotions have on well-being. The roots of EI, however, date back to 1872 when Charles Darwin's renowned work, *The Expression of the Emotions in Man and Animals,* revealed the importance of emotional expression for survival and adaptation.

In the Emotional Dimension, you will discover that the power of an emotionally healthy mindset and attitude is *essential.* The way you face ageing depends on how you prepare for it, so the sooner you start equipping yourself, the better!

Gearing Yourself Up

Age is often associated with a decline in brain function. However, research indicates that most forms of learning and retaining knowledge are well preserved with age and though all brain cells change, mental decline is *not* inevitable. Mental deterioration, such as Alzheimer's, one of the most feared consequences of ageing, can be largely prevented simply by living an intellectually-stimulating life.

Mental well-being can be enhanced by:

- Connecting and sharing your experience
- Embracing diversity

- Accepting different viewpoints
- Learning new things
- Nurturing your curiosity.

Stimulating your brain is what the Intellectual Dimension is all about. You will challenge yourself and discover simple solutions to ensure that you are ready to conquer senior life, as Geared-up intellectually as you are physically and emotionally.

Your Non-Material Belongings

Think of Spirituality as the anchor of your life; the bond between who you are, what you're made of and who you will become. Your legacy.

You need this bond to align yourself with the non-material core of your existence. It will help you stay grounded as you gain momentum with serenity, balance and purpose.

Existence takes on new meaning in the last third of our lives. After years of ups and downs, now is the ideal opportunity to observe through experienced eyes and connect with your true — maybe new — purpose. Even older adults who are sceptics about spirituality sense that there is something beyond themselves, something bigger that inspires and stimulates hope.

The Spiritual Dimension will explore gratitude, mindfulness, relationships, faith and how to make the best of your life.

Your Material Essentials

Running out of money in later years is the number one fear for many. Some even find it more fearful than dying.

This means, *now* is more important than ever to make sure you feel financially sound, including the ability to manage commitments, to protect yourself and your loved ones against risks and to prepare for future needs.

17

However, that's only one part of your story. Your relationship and beliefs around money and how you choose to spend it changes throughout life. Now is the perfect time to realign.

The Financial Dimension explores your material needs and wants. You'll discover what kind of spender you are and, most importantly, decide what type of spender you want to become, calibrated to your physical, intellectual, emotional and spiritual Gears.

Awake? Ready to Shake-Up and Thrive?

Please pick up and refer to this book anytime you're yearning for inspiration or guidance. We've organized chapters in the order that our experience tells us makes sense. However, you might be ready to jump directly to your most needy Dimension now. That means you've already awakened something and are ready to elevate and flourish. Go for it!

Advance at your own pace, revising or repairing each Gear until you feel satisfied and ready to move on. To encourage and inspire you, we've included *real stories* of people like you who are just a few bold steps ahead on their journey.

You will discover our *Swiss Touch* along with our *Green Thumbs* throughout your reading.

You will recognize our *Swiss Touch* whenever you see this:

Green Thumbs will show up like this:

In the *Thrive-Guide*, at the end of this book, you'll discover a range of resources to make your intentions come to life and keep your Wake-Up, Shake-Up, Thrive! momentum powerful long after you've finished reading.

3

Physical

Physical health is one of the main preoccupations of your age group. Even if it's not (yet) your worry, you are well aware that without good health, everything in life becomes more challenging at any age. After all, if you don't feel good, how can you be or do your best?

The Physical Dimension is *the* foundation for cool ageing at its best. It's the first Gear to revise to keep your personal timepiece running smoothly; the gateway from which the other Dimensions turn and flourish.

The word *ageing* implies universal, irreversible and inevitable changes that occur to our bodies. This includes annoying things like wrinkles, age spots, more body fat and less vision. We can try to make these natural evolutions easier to accept with Botox, silly diets or glasses, but we cannot stop them from happening. Think about it: are there any statistics of countries with the least wrinkled or skinniest elderly population? Of course not, and who would care if there were?

Exceptional years beyond 50 are not about stopping the natural ageing process or adding *years to life*. Exceptional ageing is about adding *life to years* by tapping into the best of you. The cool you, however you define that. Let's shake-up your mindset and focus where change really matters to generate *your* abundant life.

Healthy ageing can be accessed through simple habits and routines around nutrition, physical activity and sleep. Whether managing your current or future health, it's never too late to learn new habits and even reverse the hands on the watch. This chapter will help you understand the importance and relevance of new health behaviors on age and how to build them to feel amazing along the way.

Nutrition to Fuel the Journey

"Eat real food. Not too much. Mostly plants." Michael
Pollan

Non-Communicable Diseases (NCDs) such as heart disease, stroke, cancer, diabetes and lung disease, are more common with age. Though often considered inevitable, research shows that NCD's are largely preventable with good nutrition. You really *are* what you eat!

What's more, nutrition can have a significant impact on overall well-being, from improved concentration to better brain function and performance. According to The World Health Organization, optimal nourishment can raise national productivity levels by up to 20%. Beyond preventing illness, nutrition is also the key to fighting obesity, an increasing global concern for many.

This quick quiz will kick-start your Nutrition Dimension discovery and help you see if it's time to shake-up your food!

1. How aware are you of what you're *supposed to eat* after age 50 for optimal health?
2. How close to your ideal weight are you?
3. What does it mean if you sometimes eat when you're bored, tired, angry, stressed or not hungry?

Nutrition to Add Life to Your Years

Everybody's looking for the *right* diet. Well, DIET is a four-letter word starting with DIE. Nobody wants that too soon, so let's focus on the core food choices and number one choice of nutrition lifestyle for healthy ageing and quality of life: Mediterranean.

Mediterranean refers to a real-food, deprivation-free *lifestyle* common in Greece, Spain, France, Italy and other countries around the Mediterranean Sea, and Switzerland. It emphasizes fruits and vegetables, nuts, grains, olive oil, poultry and seafood — and limited red meat. It includes one to two glasses of red wine per day (yay!), excludes processed and industrialized foods and encourages physical activity in its philosophy. A Mediterranean lifestyle is not a DIE-t but a very cool, *holistic* approach to life.

Eating Mediterranean-style has been found to:

- Be the anti-ageing approach most recommended by doctors
- Promote heart health, keep the brain sharp, reduce cancer risk, inflammation and frailty
- Best prevent and control non-communicable diseases — the leading cause (70%) of premature death globally.

As you explore the Mediterranean lifestyle, remember that what really matters is not the *right food*, but the *right food for you*. This simple mind shift can help you go from knowing what to do to actually doing it. Following the Mediterranean lifestyle, your life, your plate, your refrigerator, and your supermarket cart should look something like this:

Mediterranean Diet Pyramid

Swiss Touch: In Switzerland there is a genuine concern about food origin. It's not a trend or fad, but a source of pride that our culture values fresh, unprocessed, locally produced foods. Quality of food is something we strive for. Just imagine ageing with quality time and quality food...the Swiss way.

Fruit and Vegetables Equal Half Your Life...and Your Plate

With approximately 40% of adults being overweight and 13% obese, one of the most common concerns for people over 50 is weight management. Your simple solution begins here: ensure that HALF your food is composed of fruit and vegetables. As you do so, less healthy foods will be crowded-out, balancing calories, hunger and weight.

Beyond weight concerns, some specific (and bothersome) troubles of ageing such as digestive issues, water retention, and blood sugar imbalance can be prevented by adequate fruit and vegetable consumption.

The Mediterranean lifestyle proves that fruits and vegetables are *the* most vital part of optimal nutrition. Variety and quality are also more important than ever because the body's absorption of nutrients is not the same as in younger years.

One of the greatest benefits of eating fruits and vegetables is fiber; a carbohydrate found in plants such as beans, fruit, grains, nuts, and vegetables. Research has shown that older people who eat fiber-rich diets, such as the Mediterranean diet, are 80% more likely to stay healthier and live longer than those who don't. Fiber helps fight several disorders including Alzheimer's, high cholesterol, heart disease and diabetes.

Diet trends in the Western world show that older Americans consume less than 50% of recommended dietary fiber and in the UK, only 9% of adults eat enough!

So, have you checked if fruits and vegetables make up half your food?

Green Thumb: How food is grown can have a major impact on health as well as on the environment. Organic food contains less pesticides and chemicals and is frequently more nutritious than non-organic options. People with food allergies, for example, often discover their symptoms lessen or disappear when they eat only organically. Studies have found that, though non-organic fruits and vegetables offer similar levels of many nutrients, organic varieties deliver 20-40% more antioxidants: a secret to healthy ageing! There are other benefits worth considering when buying organic, locally grown fruits and vegetables: greater seasonal freshness and quality, preservative free because they don't require treatment to endure lengthy transport and encouraging local production and to keep money within your community.

VERONIKA'S JOURNEY

"By simply increasing my fruits and vegetables to be half of my food, I crowded-out my old, less healthy choices. I saw improvements in my skin, energy, sleep, immunity and weight! If I had known it could be so simple, I never would have spent 40+ years in search of some magic formula."

The 'Whole' Truth About Carbohydrates

For years people have feared carbohydrates claiming weight gain worries. Yet, carbs are the body's main fuel source and a crucial part of a healthy diet at every age. They deliver glucose, which is converted into energy for bodily functions and physical activity. In the absence of carbohydrates, your body will use protein and fat for energy, which in the long term could mean you don't get enough nutrients.

However, not all carbohydrates are equally healthy. Choosing the right quality and quantity is critical.

The healthiest sources of carbohydrates are unprocessed or minimally processed *whole* grains, vegetables, fruits and beans. *Whole* varieties provide maximum vitamins, minerals, fiber, and many phytonutrients crucial to healthy ageing.

The least healthy carbs are found in white bread, pastries, sweet drinks, and other *highly processed* foods. These are quickly converted into sugar and can contribute to weight gain, diabetes and heart disease. Have no fear! Carbohydrates will *not* cause weight gain unless consumed excessively. Your fist is the best determinant of your *portion* of carbs in most cases. The bigger the person, the bigger the fist. Healthy carbs with every meal help keep energy high and cravings low.

How *whole* and healthy are your carbs today?

Heads-Up for Hydration — Inside and Out

Despite noticing that drinking enough water makes us feel more energetic, eat less, and think faster, it's one of those habits that both of us have a hard time doing consistently. How about you?

Our bodies and brains are 70% water. The challenge is, as you age, your body retains less water and signs of thirst are milder, so, you may not feel thirsty until you're significantly dehydrated. Proper hydration has been proven to boost cognitive health, speed mental processes and stave off dementia and memory loss. Just imagine how cool it is, that you can enhance your Intellectual Dimension with H2O!

Beyond improving cognitive function and hydration, drinking enough water is one of the easiest ways to keep yourself looking younger. Water replenishes skin tissue, increases its elasticity, and delays the onset of wrinkles and fine lines.

Cheers (Santé) to Alcohol!

One to two glasses of wine per day can be a pleasant feature of the Mediterranean diet. Sensible alcohol consumption can help reduce the risk of cardiovascular disease and overall mortality rates tend to be slightly lower among moderate drinkers than abstainers. Evidence supports that alcohol, when consumed responsibly, can be an enjoyable part of a healthy lifestyle.

However, with age, alcohol can cause dehydration, wrinkly skin, impair energy levels, and add significant empty calories. It can also jeopardize coordination and judgement and perturb sleep. As we grow older, the metabolizing of alcohol slows down. The longer it lingers, the more alcohol builds up in your bloodstream, putting you at greater risk for damaging your liver, immune system, brain and mood. Moderation is key.

Swiss Touch: Despite a legal drinking age of 16, Switzerland has fewer problems with alcohol abuse than most countries. Did you know that Santé and Salute in our national languages translates as to our health?

Cheers to moderation!

The Buzz on Coffee

We love coffee!

Coffee is considered to be quite healthy thanks to high levels of antioxidants and beneficial nutrients. Studies show that coffee drinkers have a significantly lower risk of heart failure, stroke and coronary heart disease.

However, we need to ensure adequate hydration if we're coffee drinkers because its caffeine can cause excess fluid loss. Caffeine's stimulatory effects can also cause sleep perturbations or anxiety for some people. Once again, observing and understanding how your body reacts to coffee is your first step to shifting your habit. For most people, three to four cups of coffee per day can be both enjoyable and healthy.

How's your hydration? Alcohol? Coffee? When's the last time you checked?

Green Thumb: The Water Project says that the environmental cost of the huge number of discarded plastic water bottles has led some local governments to consider banning its sale. The facts speak for themselves: Plastic bottles take over 1,000 years to biodegrade and if incinerated, they produce toxic fumes. It's estimated that over 80% of all single-use water bottles used in the U.S. become litter. Only one out of five bottles are recycled. Landfills are overflowing with millions of tons of discarded water bottles. It's estimated that three liters of water are used to package one liter of bottled water. Depending on the water quality in your area, tap water is the most sustainable solution.

The Power(s) of Protein

Did you know that proteins require more energy than carbs or fats for your body to absorb? While your body is slowly assimilating proteins, they linger and keep you full for longer. Longer satiety can help you avoid snacking, cravings and manage your weight more easily.

We cannot survive without protein. It's an essential component of every cell in the body responsible for building bone, muscle, skin, hair, blood, tissues and hormones, just to name a few.

With age, there's higher risk of loss of muscle mass, strength and function; especially critical for balance and mobility. Proteins are, therefore, key nutrients for vibrant ageing.

Protein originates either from animals or plants. Animal proteins include meats, poultry, fish and seafood, eggs and dairy. Plant proteins include nuts, seeds, legumes and beans as well as some grains and cereals.

You can estimate your daily recommended protein by multiplying .8 grams of protein for every kilogram of your body weight per day. For example, if you weigh 80 kilos, you should aim to consume about 64 grams of protein daily.

However, don't forget that no food is made of 100% protein. For example, 100 grams of chicken provides approximately 15 grams of protein. Most packaged foods have labels indicating how much protein they contain.

As a rule of thumb, your fist is a good measure of protein portion size — think 1 yogurt, 1 piece of fish and so on — scattered throughout your day.

Are you getting enough protein? Do you even know?

> *Green Thumb.* Food impacts not only humans, but the planet! Agriculture is a major contributor of greenhouse gas emissions which are driving climate change. Animal-based foods — red meat in particular — tend to have higher emissions than plant-based.

For example, eggs are among one of the healthiest and most nutritious animal proteins you can eat, whichever type you choose. Here are some *green* considerations: #1 Choice: Pastured eggs: Chickens allowed to roam free, eating natural and some commercial feed. #2 Choice: Omega-3-enriched eggs: Conventional chickens with feed supplemented with an omega-3 source like flax. The next best choice because they are richer in vitamins A, D, E, and omega-3s. #3 Choice: Organic eggs: The hens were not treated with hormones and received organic feed, so antibiotic-free. #4 Choice: Conventional eggs: Standard store-bought eggs from hens that are usually fed grain, supplemented with vitamins and minerals.

Fat Facts versus Fiction

Did you know that fat from food is an *essential* source of energy and body endurance, especially in older years? Fat helps your body absorb vitamins and minerals, build cell membranes like skin, promotes brain health and reduces disease risk. Healthy fats literally improve the ageing of every part of your body.

However, many have misunderstood fat since the 1970's when researchers began linking it with heart disease and excess weight, likely because fat contains double the calories of carbohydrates or protein. As a result, by the 80's and 90's, many nutrition organizations and governments encouraged low-fat diets. Unfortunately, this trend backfired, leading to more overweight, obesity, diabetes and heart disease than ever!

It's useful to understand the three categories of Fat in terms of health benefits: Mono and Poly-unsaturated, Saturated, Industrial-made trans fats.

Mono and Poly-unsaturated fats are healthy fats that come mainly from vegetables, nuts, seeds, and fish. They're encouraged in the Mediterranean diet, usually in the form of oils. Omega-3 fatty acids are also in this category. They have been linked to people living longer and healthier lives. Older adults with the highest blood levels of omega-3's are most likely to live free of chronic diseases, mental or physical deterioration. Omega-3 fatty acids are found in fish such as salmon, mackerel, sardines, as well as flaxseeds, walnuts, canola oil, and un-hydrogenated soybean oil.

Saturated fats are solid at room temperature. They are present in red meat, whole dairy products and widespread industrially prepared foods such as cakes and cookies. A diet rich in these fats can drive up weight, cholesterol and heart disease. Most nutrition experts recommend limiting saturated fat to under 10% of daily calories.

30

Industrial-made Trans Fats are a byproduct of a process called hydrogenation which turns oils into solids to prevent them from becoming rancid. Trans fats are considered the worst type of fat because they raise bad cholesterol while lowering good cholesterol and increase heart disease risk. Trans fats have no known health benefits and there is no safe level of consumption. They have even been banned in some countries.

WILLIAM'S JOURNEY

William, a 58-year-old corporate lawyer, had a great exercise routine, healthy nutrition and work-life balance. Yet, he couldn't understand why his weight and high blood pressure persisted despite his efforts. By working with Ellen and tracking his weekly food intake, he realized that he was *mindlessly* consuming peanuts every evening in front of the television. When he discovered that those 800 calories represented almost one third of his daily calorie needs and four times the recommended amount of saturated fat, he decided to cut back. On his next check-up, William's weight and blood pressure were significantly down. All thanks to skipping peanuts!

Green Thumb: Organic versus Conventional Oils. *Organic* certification is strictly regulated and differs slightly between countries. This certification requires time, money and effort. The difference between organic oil and conventional oil is in the farming and manufacturing. Traditionally, premium olive oils, for example, are grown and harvested *identically* to the olives used in organic olive oil. More often than not, the only actual difference between certified organic olive oil and premium extra virgin olive oil is the monitoring that earns the oil its certification. So, premium quality, cold-pressed are what to look for when best choosing oils, rather than organic.

Your Cholesterol Check

Your body needs cholesterol to build healthy cells, but high levels of cholesterol can increase risks of heart disease, heart attack or stroke. High cholesterol can be inherited, but it's often the result of unhealthy lifestyle choices, which often make it often preventable and treatable.

Before 2017, your doctor would have likely said to avoid foods high in cholesterol, such as eggs. Today, we know that the cholesterol from diet has little effect on our heart health and that giving up cholesterol-rich foods altogether is not usually beneficial. A much better way to influence your *cholesterol factory* is to adopt a Mediterranean lifestyle including regular body movement and healthy weight maintenance.

Green Thumb: Organic versus Conventional Dairy. Organic dairy comes from cows that have not been treated with antibiotics and are produced under country-specific sustainability and pesticide rules. Advantages include: better animal welfare because cows graze freely, no antibiotics or hormones (which raise health risks in humans), a higher nutritional content such as vitamin E and beta-carotene, more omega-3 fatty acids and antioxidants, a longer shelf life due to processing at ultrahigh temperatures and more abundant wildlife and biodiversity around organic farms.

Is Food About Behaving Well or Feeling Well?

"When I'm hungry, I eat what I love. When I'm bored, I do something I love. When I'm lonely, I connect with someone I love. When I feel sad, I remember that I am loved." Dr. Michelle May

If you've read and understood the nutrition concepts above, you likely have a pretty clear idea of how to *behave well with your food* in your third life chapter. What if you ate to *feel well* rather than to *behave well*? What if, instead of focusing on *what you should* eat, you tapped into your expert within to discover *why, when, how and how much* you eat? Doesn't that sound cooler and more empowering than listening to someone's else's rules?

At this age, you likely have ingrained habits and attitudes when it comes to what and how you eat. Pausing to think about what you put in your mouth takes some effort. It's been recognized, however, that applying simple principles of mindful eating can have a positive impact on overall well-being and help with weight management. Mindful eating is an approach that helps you take charge of your eating habits — whatever you choose to eat.

Mindful eating begins by pausing to ask a simple question: why do I eat? The likely answer would be, because *I need to* or because *I'm hungry*. But are you really? Might you be eating out of habit, boredom or fatigue? Influenced by the people around you or seeking to comfort stress? We were all born with the instinctive capability to eat when we're hungry and stop when we're full. You can observe this with young children. Understanding why you eat and distinguishing between real hunger and non-hunger triggers takes practice.

Mindful eating is about slowing down to eat without distraction to listen to physical hunger cues until you feel satisfied and better than before you ate. How unsatisfying it is to love a food so much that you actually overeat to the point that you feel too full, guilty or regretful afterwards. Eating more mindfully, and engaging your senses heightens your awareness of colors, smells, textures, and flavors. It also allows you to notice the effects food has on your feelings which will be further explored in the Emotional Dimension. As you practice eating more mindfully, it will gradually replace your *automatic pilot* with more conscious, healthier responses and help you reconnect with your instinct.

Swiss Touch. The Swiss pride themselves on eating delicious food and savoring it mindfully. In social, business, school and home life, the Swiss prefer not to eat alone and take time to savor both the food and the moment. School and work breaks are mandatory, and families still eat together a great majority of the time. In 2020, children, and many parents, still return home from school or work for lunch. Numerous studies have confirmed that when we sit down to take time for meals in the company of family or friends, we enjoy more and eat less. Doesn't that sound like a nice way to grow older?

SUZANNE'S JOURNEY

Suzanne struggled with yo-yo dieting for over 20 years. She experienced regret-repent-repeat every time she *failed to behave well* on her many restrictive diets. She was fed up! When she began applying the principles of mindful eating to her food (and life), she stopped stressing about *what* to eat and started listening to herself. Slowing down, listening to her body, following her instincts pulled her out of guilt-mode and empowered her to make better decisions. Her eating habits went gradually from excessive and restrictive to instinctive. She is living more intuitively than she has since her youth. At 55, she has lost 14 kilos and still claims, "I have no idea how I did that!"

The great thing about shifting your mindset about your food choices and how you eat, is, the more you do it, the easier it gets. Gradually, new habits replace old ones and those that make you *truly feel well* become lasting reflexes.

In the *Thrive-Guide* you will find strategies for nutrition and for tapping into your *expert within* to eat more mindfully forever.

Movement: No Time Left Not to

"Physical activity is the easiest manner to avoid practically all chronic illness." World Health Organization

---

A Harvard Alumni study suggests that those who exercise regularly gain about two hours of life expectancy for every hour of exercise. This means you can actually influence how long you live by moving your butt!

Physical activity can help prevent heart disease, cancer, stroke, hypertension, diabetes, osteoporosis and even Alzheimer's. It also benefits mobility, balance, flexibility, sleep, eating habits, mood, stress, body mass and brain function. Goodbye *senior moments*!

The bottom line: regular movement slows the ageing process and promotes a longer, healthier, more vigorous life.

A well-rounded exercise program should include Aerobic-Cardiovascular Activity, Resistance Training and Flexibility. The World Health Organization recommends doing a moderate-intensity Aerobic-Cardiovascular activity for a minimum of 30 minutes per day and Resistance or Strength training sessions two or more times a week.

Just in case you're wondering *which* activity is best, it's whichever you enjoy enough to do regularly — non-negotiable — for the rest of your life.

This quick quiz will kick-start your Physical Activity Dimension journey and help you discover if it's time for some shaking-up!

1. Are you aware of changes in physical activity you should make after 50?
2. How often do you get 10,000 steps a day?
3. How often do you get flexibility, endurance and weight-bearing exercise?

Add Life to Years with Aerobic-Cardiovascular Activity

Cardiovascular diseases are the number one cause of death globally, taking an estimated 18 million lives every year. That's huge! One third of these deaths occur prematurely in people under seventy and most are preventable. Aerobic or cardiovascular activity is, therefore, the *most* important type of movement as we age.

Cardio includes all activity that raises your heart rate. Intervals as short as 10-minutes are impactful. Examples include dancing, walking, swimming, cycling or tennis. Incidental regular movement like vacuuming, washing windows, climbing stairs or gardening count too. In fact, you won't find people in the Blue Zones — specific areas in the world where a higher than usual number of people live much longer than average — actually exercising much but simply moving energetically throughout their days.

When was the last time you checked how many steps you get daily?

Cardio takes care of your heart; however, heart health is not only about the organ. Your heart is also at the core of your emotions. Negative emotions can strain your heart leading to serious health problems. Positive heart-felt emotions like love, care, appreciation, and compassion, help your heart age better.

Swiss Touch: Almost half of the Swiss are active hikers or walkers tallying up an average of 9650 steps per day — almost double the American average. Walking is so embedded in the culture, that if Swiss trails were to be laid end-to-end, they would circle the globe 1.5 times!

Add Life to Your Years with Flexibility

Flexibility includes stretching activities that lengthen your muscles and help keep you supple as you age. Depending on your preferences, this could be stretching, yoga, Tai Chi, Pilates or strength training. Flexibility improves pain, injuries, posture, balance, strength and resilience. A spontaneous morning stretch can be a simple yet impactful ritual to increase blood flow, flexibility and start your day recharged.

So, how limber are you feeling today and how flexible is your mindset about changing that?

Add Life to Your Years with Resistance or Strength Training

How can you resist?

Resistance exercises cause muscles to contract against some external force. Weightlifting, push-ups, squats or resistance bands increase muscle and joint strength, making every-day tasks as easy as they were when you were younger.

In addition, strength training improves common senior issues of flexibility, balance, weight management, stamina, mobility, posture, and bone density.

LAURINE'S JOURNEY

"I was 57 when I attended one of Ellen's workshops on lifestyle and stress management. Though, it started out of pure curiosity, it ended up changing my life and saving me money! I found myself sitting among women who were confessing to eating chips and chocolates. I wondered to myself, *what am I doing here? I don't have these bad habits.* Then Ellen spoke about the importance of daily walking, encouraging us to aim for 10.000 steps per day.

Inspired, I decided to start counting my steps the next day. When I only clocked 600 steps on day one, 10,000 seemed a faraway goal. However, I started walking to the office and taking the train everywhere and gradually my habits changed. Since my car was sitting idle in the garage, I gave up my paid parking space and realized

I no longer needed a gym membership tallying up all those steps. Today, I log an average of 15,000 steps a day and save about $5000 a year! I manage my weight, feel younger, happier and less stressed than ever."

Green Thumb: Ecology and Physical Activity. A report by the WHO defends that inactivity accounts for increasing deaths and disability worldwide. They suggest that increasing physical activity is vital to achieve global targets on the prevention of premature mortality from noncommunicable diseases and to halt the obesity epidemic. To mitigate these inactivity risks, the WHO is actively promoting public spaces in cities that encourage *active outdoor life and active ecological mobility.* Since a great majority of the global population is expected to live in urban areas by 2030 these initiatives are great drivers of sustainable change for healthy lives and well-being for all.

Refer to your *Thrive-Guide* to discover how and which types of cardio, flexibility and resistance activities you should consider after 50.

Sleep Your Way to Your Dream Life

"Sleep may be more essential than food; animals die of sleep deprivation before starvation!" Dragana Rogula
for National Geographic

Did you know that insufficient sleep is considered to be a global public health epidemic and that over 60% of adults feel they don't sleep well?

Most people tend to underestimate the restorative power of sleep and electronic devices seem to be worsening the situation. Whether sleep is a problem for you or not, you know how beneficial a good night's rest is for operating at your best.

Sleep adds life to your years by its profound impact on overall health, hormones, immunity and brain function. It improves learning capacity, memory and attention, problem solving and creativity. That's *calibrating* your intellectual and emotional Gears while in slumber.

Insufficient sleep is one of the main causes of accidents, mistakes and lapses in reasoning and judgement. It's also a source of irritability, slower reaction times and irrationality, all of which *could* be (and often are) blamed on ageing. Even premature mortality has been linked to poor sleep. It's time to wake-up and instead of blaming *senior moments* for your slip-ups, maybe you just need to take a snooze.

According to Matthew Walker, Author of *Why We Sleep,* there are three major changes to your sleep after age 50:

First, the quantity and the quality of your sleep is reduced. This is due to the natural reduction of deep non-rapid eye movement sleep (NREM) sleep. You obtain fewer hours of deep sleep and NREM brain waves become smaller, less powerful, and fewer in number. By 50, you've been stripped of 60-70% of the deep sleep you enjoyed as a teen and by age 70, you will have lost 80-90% of your youthful deep sleep.

Second, the efficiency of your sleep is diminished. The older you get, the more frequently you wake up throughout the night. Due to sleep fragmentation, many older adults suffer a reduction in sleep efficiency — how much sleep you actually get while in bed. Most doctors consider a sleep efficiency of 90% good sleep. As a reference, healthy teenagers enjoy a sleep efficiency of about 95% and by 80 this drops to below 70 or 80%. Sleep efficiency affects physical health, energy, cognitive function, depression and even mortality risk.

Finally, your sleep timing is disrupted. Due to natural earlier evening release and peak of melatonin — the hormone that manages your circadian-sleep rhythms — sleep is instructed to start earlier. This regression in sleep timing leads to earlier and earlier bedtimes, thus the *early bird specials* many restaurants promote in retirement communities. This disrupted timing can cause a sleep debt if you fight nature and try to be cool and stay up later even though your body will automatically wake you up earlier.

So, it's normal to sleep a little less, a little earlier, and less deeply as we age. However, experts assert that the majority of sleep problems in older adults are related to physical and mental health issues and most of these problems can be resolved through healthy lifestyle habits. Early to bed, early to rise…

Green Thumb: Eco-Friendly Sleep means sleeping with less contamination. Decreased exposure to toxins promotes higher quality, and perhaps even quantity, sleep. Some green-sleep ideas to think about: 100% natural organic mattress and bed linens, bed made of recycled materials, wood furniture, organic paint, air-purifying plants.

CARLA'S JOURNEY

At 60, Carla was knowledgeable about nutrition, but had struggled with her weight, cravings and lack of energy for years. By having a closer look at her habits, we discovered that she averaged five to six hours of sleep per night. That likely explained her lack of energy! When she discovered that screen-time, household chores and family bickering prevented her from getting to bed before midnight, she realized she needed to prioritize her sleep routine.

By opening up to family support, turning off her computer and decluttering her bedroom, Carla ramped-up her sleep to seven and then eventually to eight hours. It led her to lose one kilo per month over the next six months and dissolve the fatigue that was driving her cravings, over-eating and struggling relationships.

Sleep requirements vary from person to person, but most healthy adults require between seven and nine hours per night to thrive. The key to waking up feeling rested and energetic is to discover the number of hours that best works for *you*. A great way to test this is to observe how long you sleep after a few days without schedules and commitments, such as weekends or vacation time.

Burnout rates have never been higher and go hand-in-hand with lack of sleep. Many organizations have recognized this as well as the benefits of rest on productivity. Subsequently, they now promote workplace recuperation through breaks, flextime or naps. *The more I stress the less I sleep, the less I sleep, the more I stress* is a vicious cycle at any age.

This quick quiz will help reveal how much you already prioritize your sleep.

1. How often do you wake up in the morning without using an alarm?
2. How often do you sleep the same number of hours on workdays and days off?
3. How aware are you of age-appropriate sleep habits for optimal health?

Swiss Touch: Swiss are living proof that good life balance depends on prioritizing rest and recuperation, and it's embedded in their culture. Minimum breaks away from the workplace are required throughout the day and the percentage of employees working very long hours is lower than the European average. Employees are entitled to a minimum of 20 days off each year, plus public holidays and everyone must be granted a rest period of at least 11 consecutive hours weekly, and 35 over weekends. The cool truth is that the

Swiss *really do* take their rest seriously and actually take time off.

Your *Thrive-Guide* provides practices to choose from to adapt your rest, recovery, and sleep to your age. A lifetime dream come true!

Physical Shake-Up Wrap-Up

"To keep the body in good health is a duty, otherwise we shall not be able to keep our mind strong and clear." Buddha

Remember:

- A Mediterranean Lifestyle is a great option for ageing well
- It's not only about what you eat, but why, how, when and how much
- Never DIE-t
- Move your body an hour a day, for the rest of your life, non-negotiable
- Cardio, Flexibility and Endurance activities promote youthful ageing
- Expect sleep patterns to change with age
- How you age is directly influenced by your sleep
- Nutrition and movement affect sleep and vice-versa
- It's never too late to galvanize your physical well-being!

Elevate Now!

Starting now, *track* your physical well-being. Use an App, website, or hand-written journal to begin tracking your food, movement, and sleep. Observe your patterns and take advantage of data comparisons to assess where you are now. Remember, to manage any change successfully, you must start with know where you begin.

Stuff we love to track:

- Activity trackers that count beyond steps and include yoga, walking or gardening
- Food trackers that calculate macro- and micro-nutrients as well as calorie comparisons and weight management

- Sleep trackers that monitor what time you go to sleep, wake-up and how you feel when you awaken
- Habit Apps that nudge with personalized notifications.

Though this chapter ends, it's only a beginning to understanding your Five Dimensions which your *Thrive-Guide* will bring to life with simple, practical habit tweaks.

4

Emotional

"Life is short. Break the rules. Forgive quickly. Kiss slowly. Love truly. Laugh uncontrollably and never regret anything that makes you smile." Mark Twain

---

Maybe that quote made you smile, awakening some emotion deep inside you. Maybe not. Each of us is unique in our feelings, without exception.

Earlier in our book we discovered the Physical Dimension, the *base-camp* of your journey. Think of the Emotional Dimension as your *equipment*: the essential tools and strategies that allow you to best manage life's ups and downs. Negative emotions — the downs — usually require the most coping, but positive emotions — the ups — need attention, too. Though the negatives are often seen as *bad* and the positives *good*, the truth is, that experiencing, practicing and perfecting both is the only way to reach emotional well-being. Imagine you only knew how to express your disappointment and not your joy, or to share feelings of love and not grief.

Emotional well-being is a combination of your thoughts and feelings, the relationship you have with your inner self and how you relate to the world. You can think of your emotions as E-nergy in M-otion. Some emotions will drive your energy, others will drain it.

Emotions play a central role in every *human* life from the moment we're born until the day we die. They prepare our body for action and guide more than 90% of our decisions and behaviors. Since emotions are so vital to daily functioning, it's important to understand how ageing influences them.

Research shows that emotions are relatively unaffected or even improve with age. Older age has been associated with improved emotional stability and feeling happy more often.

In fact, older adults show social and emotional functioning equal to or superior to younger adults. We tend to fly off the handle less and dare laugh more. One of our clients, for example, stated, "At 52, I finally feel true relief embracing my imperfections and vulnerability."

However, these age-related emotional advantages appear to be compromised when faced with prolonged stress, so it's especially important to prioritize stress management and mental balance as you age.

Studies have shown that your emotional *mindset* is important, too. Those who *view* ageing as an adaptation rather than as an uncontrollable state, show significantly improved stamina and resilience.

In many countries, including Switzerland, nurturing, listening to and expressing emotions is not what we're taught. There is an imposed and acceptable reserve and discretion about communicating emotions, whether positive or negative. Swiss self-assuredly say, "Don't worry, I'm fine," when the truth is, one cannot and does not always recognize what *fine* really is. We've worked with jobless clients, especially men, who struggle to express their emotional disappointment. One example is of a man who buried and hid his emotions: he dressed and pretended to go to *work* for months, too ashamed to admit he had been laid off. Once he accepted his desperate emotional state and was given the space to express it, he felt more confident and better able to focus on his job search.

Putting words to feelings and identifying your emotions are the first steps to aligning with your beliefs, values and priorities. Yet, we've noticed that most people cannot even describe their emotions. Though some people are better than others at nurturing emotional balance, you can learn to develop it at any age. We want to help you discover and develop those emotions that will best serve you in your third chapter.

How do you really *feel* today? Do you even remember the vocabulary to express it?

This quick quiz will help you position yourself emotionally. Your answers will reveal if this Dimension is ready for some shaking-up!

1. How easy is it for you to *name* precisely the many emotions you feel throughout the day?
2. How confident do you feel about managing your emotions, whether negative or positive?
3. How quickly do you tend to bounce back after a disappointment or stumbling over an obstacle?

The Iceberg

Imagine one of your loved ones *forgets* to fill the car with gas or to empty the dishwasher. You sigh, frustrated, and end up doing *their* task. You don't say anything — it's not worth the bother. The next time they ask you for any favor you overreact aggressively — still resentful about that previous event.

What happened? You managed the obstacle — the gas or the dishes — but didn't notice the emotions building-up inside. Like an iceberg where you could only see the tip, you navigated around it with no idea how much lies beneath.

The hidden parts of the iceberg are invisible, so we often assume they don't exist and, consequently, don't develop coping strategies to navigate around them. They later show up as frustration, resentment or anger and contribute to faster ageing. Modern science tells us that awareness, understanding and naming our emotions are the first steps in bringing them to the surface to see and deal with them. Practice improves your navigation around all the inevitable icebergs of life.

The good news is that it's never too late!

Name It to Tame It

"When awareness is brought to an emotion, power is brought to your life." Tara Meyer Robson

---

To start using your emotional equipment, you need to understand what's in your backpack. Despite 50+ years of experience, we're not always good at describing what's in there — our feelings. Think about it-, if you can't clearly describe the pain, how can your doctor help?

Naming our emotions, especially negative ones, tends to lessen the burden they might create. Dan Siegel, renowned professor of psychiatry and neurobiology, refers to this practice as *name it to tame it*. Noticing and naming emotions gives you the opportunity to step back and choose what to do with them. Whether at home or at work, managing emotions can be done practically by *naming them.*

Matthew D. Lieberman of UCLA found that putting feelings into words makes sadness, anger and pain less intense. He explains, "When you put feelings into words, you're activating this prefrontal region and seeing a reduced response in the amygdala. In the same way you hit the brake when you're driving, and you see a yellow light — when you put feelings into words — you seem to be hitting the brakes on your emotional responses. As a result, a person may feel less angry or less sad."

As you learn to identify, label and verbally express your emotions, your brain becomes stronger and better at responding more *proactively* and less *reactively* to life events. Science validates that naming and sharing emotions also nurtures meaningful relationships and connections — among the greatest sources of happiness and longevity.

There are very few basic emotions but many nuances. Dr Robert Plutchik, grouped general emotional responses into *Eight Primary Emotions*: *Joy, Sadness, Fear, Disgust, Surprise, Anticipation, Anger and Trust*. Nuances of *Fear* might include *Apprehension* or *Terror*, while

Anger could be broken down into *Annoyance* or *Rage*. Plutchik argued for the predominance of these eight emotions because they trigger high-survival behaviors, such as the way *fear* triggers the well-known *fight-or-flight* response.

Beyond giving a name to your emotions, non-identification with them will leave you space to oversee your feelings. Compare these two expressions, 'I am sad', versus 'I notice I am feeling sad'. The first has you in the space of a victim while the latter puts you in the driver's seat.

MICHEL'S JOURNEY

When Michel came to us, his credibility and influence at work had hit rock bottom. At 53, with over ten years in the company, he was refused a new role due to his 'inappropriate' communication style.

He felt ashamed, not good enough and irritated. He didn't really understand where he'd gone wrong. He was often perceived as aggressive, stressed out, impatient and too tough.

Michel discovered that what was blocking him was his lack of confidence. He was easily offended by negative feedback and felt misunderstood by his peers. He was deep in a self-destructive vicious circle of resentment and anger that showed up at work. Once he identified his emotions and where they were coming from, he re-established self-assurance, became more relaxed and communicated with more confidence. His smile and friendliness became sincere assets to building trust. His peers and his superiors noticed the difference and he got promoted the following year.

Bias by Us

Did you know that how you think directly influences how you feel and behave? If you think you're a failure, you'll feel and act like one, reinforcing your belief that you *must be* a failure. Your thoughts are a catalyst for self-perpetuating cycles.

Once you draw a conclusion about yourself, you're likely to look for evidence that reinforces your belief while ignoring anything to the contrary. For example, someone who develops the belief that she's a failure, will view each mistake as evidence. When she does succeed, she'll chalk it up to luck.

Each of us has a set of beliefs, assumptions and thought processes that can work against our best interest. Shirzad Chamine — Positive Intelligence Authority — calls them our *Saboteurs*.

Saboteurs cross cultures, genders, and age groups and we often don't even know they exist.

Your *Judge* is the master *Saboteur* that compels you to constantly find fault with yourself, others, your conditions or circumstances. Your *Judge* generates anxiety, stress, anger, disappointment, shame and guilt.

The good news is that we also have automatic mind habits that are positive — named your *Sage* by Shirzad Chamine. Your *Sage* sees challenges as gifts and opportunities, generating increased happiness and well-being. *Sage* powers lie in a different region of your brain than the *Saboteurs*. There are specific mindset, attitude and positivity exercises to practice tapping into your *Sage* more often than your *Saboteur*.

Consider for a minute that it might not be your age that holds you back, but your *saboteur beliefs about age* that prevent you from even trying.

Ageism is a negative belief, stereotyping, prejudice, or discrimination based on age. It can affect anybody, but it often affects older adults. Understanding and combating ageism is a first step to reducing apprehension, making the world more age-friendly and simplifying your transition to older years.

Most of the time we're unaware of our bias towards ageing and older people. However, the World Values Survey of 57 countries found that 60% of people felt that older adults were not respected. How does that make *you feel*?

Ageism is demonstrated by young and old alike. The media often stereotypes older people as sweet but absent-minded. Jokes about getting older are commonly made. We often tell people that they look younger than their age, which, though meant as a compliment, implies that looking older is less desirable than looking younger. Raising awareness about our negative attitudes about ageing is a fundamental step to transforming our mindsets and reaping its benefits.

Changing how you think about getting *old* can have a profound impact on your health. Negative attitudes about ageing can damage your sense of self, reduce your opportunities, separate you from others, and actually shorten your life. WHO research shows that older adults with negative attitudes about ageing may live almost eight years less than those with positive attitudes. In a separate study at Yale, more than 600 people aged 50 and older were asked to complete a survey about their perceptions of ageing. Participants who held a positive outlook had lower instances of cardiac disease, better memory, and were more likely to recover from illness or injury than their negative counterparts.

Society often uses age in terms of *years* rather than in terms of *ability* to determine when people must stop working or give up their driver's license, for example. The assumption that all members of a group are the same — stereotyping — is always a mistake. This is especially true with age because there is no *typical* older person. The older we get, the more diverse, interesting and better we become!

Myths about ageing can even *contribute* to failing memory. Middle-aged and older learners do worse on memory tasks when exposed to negative stereotypes than when messages are positive. People who believe that they're not in control of their memory, constantly joking about *old-age forgetfulness*, for example, are less likely to work at maintaining or improving their memory. They are, therefore, more likely to experience

cognitive decline. If you believe you can improve and you put that belief into practice, you have a better chance of staying sharp.

As we outlined in the opening of this book, new research focusing on
longevity hotspots around the world found that small lifestyle changes
can add up to ten years to most people's lives and that ageing is only
25% genetic and 75% lifestyle.

Our perceptions of age determine how we age, both emotionally and
physically.

To understand how you *feel* about ageing, think about how you might
complete the following phrases:

- I'm too old to…
- It's too late in life for…
- Those…are for someone younger
- …is hard at my age.

Ageing is often a very positive experience. With age comes wisdom and
a greater understanding of the world and your place in it. Most tend to
slow down in some respects, but that doesn't mean giving up; it means
less stress and more appreciation.

Simply put, changing your beliefs about ageing can be a greater indicator of longevity than many other factors including socio-economic
background and gender.

MARC'S JOURNEY

At 54, Marc felt old, useless and miserable. He'd been mobbed out
of a job and was unhappy at home. He was emotionally abused and
was convinced *he* was to blame for his misery. By exploring how he
felt, he was able to identify the hidden emotions below the iceberg,
the nagging little voices in his head — his *Saboteurs*. Guilt, fear, anxiety and lack of self-esteem were preventing him from feeling and
being his best.

By exercising his positivity and developing his *Sage*, Marc changed his home life, reconnected with his teenage children and friends he'd neglected, and found a job he loved. By 55, Marc envisioned his future brighter than ever and, today, this once severely depressed man is an inspiration to those around him.

Choose Positive

> *"Attitude is a choice. Happiness is a choice. Optimism is a choice. Kindness is a choice. Giving is a choice. Respect is a choice. Whatever choice you make makes you. Choose wisely."* Roy T. Bennett

Positive thinking is not only about your thoughts on age and ageing, but also about your general outlook on life. Though positive emotions don't last forever, their impact can. Positive people have been shown to:

• Be less stressed
• Maintain better relationships
• Have a greater capacity to learn and be more creative.

Positivity has been shown to improve longevity, depression and resilience. People with a positive outlook are one-third less likely to have a heart attack, even those with a family history of heart disease.

Positive Intelligence (PI) measures the relative strength of control you have over your mind and how well your mind acts in your best interest. High PI means your mind acts as your friend (*Sage*) far more than as your enemy (*Saboteur*). Low PI is the opposite.

When your mind tells you that you should do your best to prepare for retirement, it's acting as your friend. When it wakes you up at night anxious about the future, worrying about everything from health to money, it's acting as your enemy.

Groundbreaking research in psychology and neuroscience shows that high PI results not only in greater happiness and performance, but longevity, too. High PI fosters enhanced immunity, lower stress, lower blood pressure, less pain, fewer colds, better sleep, and a reduced likelihood of having hypertension, diabetes or stroke.

Positive Intelligence is not about seeing everything rosy all the time, but about tapping into your *Sage* more often. Life brings us all challenges, unpleasant events and tough situations. Positivity is not about ignoring them. It's what you do with it. According to Ed Diener, distinguished Professor of Psychology, well-being is more strongly associated with the frequency and duration of positive feelings than with the intensity of those feelings. That means that everyday happy moments are more important and impactful than intense happy events. Like exercising any muscle, small, consistent stimuli, rather than big, infrequent stimuli, exercise your *Sage* muscle best. A strong *Sage* allows you to ultimately *choose your feelings.*

To illustrate choosing your feelings through exercising your *Sage*, imagine you're driving on the highway after a hard day, longing to be home. An accident happens delaying your anticipated arrival. You have two possible outlooks to choose from:

One: I'm SO frustrated!

I was so looking forward to getting home. Why does this always happen to me? Why can't people be more careful? It's not fair! My evening is ruined. The resulting *feelings* here are resentment, frustration and anger which affect not only our mood but our ageing!

Two: Wow!

Imagine, a little time difference and it could have been me in that accident. I feel grateful to be safe. I hope all is well. I'll turn up my music, call home or a friend and make the best of the wait. The resulting *feelings* here are of gratitude, calm and hope which positively affect our mental disposition and health.

Which would you choose?

If you think you tend to react more like option one, maybe it's time to consider another outlook. Positivity can be cultivated. By choosing how you react to situations, you can increase *your positivity and transform your attitude.*

In the *Thrive-Guide* you will find checklists and suggestions to help you practice and boost your positivity.

Passion Power

It is often said that a desire fueled by *passion* will bring about the greatest results in life.

Pursuing passions does wonders for ageing vibrantly. Cultivating and practicing what we *love* to do has been shown to improve sleep quality and mood, lower blood pressure, risks of heart disease, anxiety, stress and depression.

Total Brain Health is a global leader in educational wellness programs for professionals in active aging. Their cutting-edge science has proven that pursuing passions can be a buffer against memory loss. It also leads to improved neuroplasticity — the ability of the brain to form and reorganize new connections.

Gretchen Rubin of the Happiness Project provides great food for thought, "A passion gives you a reason to keep learning and to work toward mastery. It can often give you a reason to travel, and therefore to have the new experiences so key to happiness. It gives you something in common with other people, and so fosters social bonds. It gives you purpose."

Passion is an *emotion to be acted upon*. Without action, passion cannot yield results. Passion is the fuel that fires our actions to craft our dream life.

By definition, *passion* is *a willingness to suffer for what you love*. The most famous example being the passion of Jesus Christ. Your passions are, therefore, activities, subjects, or causes that you care about so much that you are willing to suffer for them.

This self-reflection may make it easier to discern whether something is truly a passion or simply a strong interest. If you're not sure, just pick something you enjoy and see if you're willing to give up other activities to spend more time on it.

Discovering or rediscovering your passions — those things that light you up, that cause you to lose track of time or that you hate to stop doing — is an adventure. When you deliberately open yourself up to noticing the things you are passionate about, you will learn, grow and have a great time doing it!

From Head to Heart

> *"As our feelings change, this mixture of peptides travels throughout your body and your brain. And they're literally changing the chemistry of every cell in your body — and sending out vibrations to other people."* Candace Pert

The Head

Did you know that our emotions are electrochemical signals that flow through us in an unending cycle? From the brain's hypothalamus to the rest of the body, it takes only six seconds to transmit each emotion. Just imagine, *only seconds* for each emotional signal to deliver a message to help us learn, grow and become a better version of ourselves.

Humans, as opposed to other animals, *feel* their environment and *interpret* it using a vast range of emotions. The part of the brain responsible for processing emotions is the *limbic brain*, also called the *emotional brain*.

Your *emotional brain* was already functional before birth and was the brain area most used until the age of nine. You were an emotional sponge during your childhood, absorbing everything through feelings.

Think of your early years. What emotions bubble up? A peaceful, positive childhood likely triggered joy, pride and love. A troubled one might

56

have generated guilt, sadness or fear. The emotions developed in these foundational years inevitably emerge from below the iceberg in adult life. Deep seeded unconscious feelings of not being *good enough* could later result in aggressivity or burnout. Guilt-driven behaviors established in childhood, might emerge as a *poor me* victim attitude.

In adulthood, like working out in the gym, exercising your emotional brain keeps it flexible and youthful. New learning and stimulating activities create a *limber-limbic* brain less prone to brain-related decline in memory and creativity.

Exercising your emotional brain through repeated, positive, intentional affirmations will subconsciously change your state of mind. Thoughts, such as, *I'm feeling peaceful,* or *I can handle whatever comes my way*, will root themselves in your head and gradually become your new reality.

In the past, psychologists believed that emotions were *only* a matter of the brain. Today, modern neuroscience tells us that the heart actually sends five times more information to the head than the head sends to the heart.

The Heart

Have you ever had your *heart broken?* That saying is not accidental. Your heart, alongside your brain, contributes to your emotional state. Your heart emits one of the strongest electromagnetic fields of all your organs, extending in every direction up to two meters outside your body. Your emotions are encoded in your energetic field allowing your heart and brain to signal each other through emotional sparks. Neuroscience is so cool.

As you experience anger, frustration or anxiety your heart rhythm becomes more erratic. These erratic patterns are sent to emotional centers in your brain which recognize them as negative or stressful. This creates the *feelings* you experience in your heart and body. Love, empathy and happiness produce a cardiac rhythm that signals your brain and heart to *feel* good.

This means that anything that can help prevent that *broken heart,* whether physical or emotional, really matters.

The Body

Your brain and heart are critical to managing your emotions, but that's not all. Neuroscience and epigenetics now prove that the brain also impacts physical health. This means that your body can be healthier through emotional wellness. Negative emotions such as anger, guilt or frustration can lead to back pain, headache, fatigue and ageing ailments. Positive emotions such as joy, happiness or empathy can promote the healing of everything from aches and pains to serious illness.

Even proper hydration makes brain and heart connections work better and faster, aligning emotions and bodily reactions. Since your brain is 75% water, adequate hydration improves focus, concentration and thinking, while inadequate water (or food) can create brain fog or confusion.

Ups and Downs

> *"The greatest glory in living lies not in never falling,*
> *but in rising every time we fall."* Nelson Mandela

At 50+, you have years of life experience with many emotional ups and downs. Try remembering your first love, getting married, a family loss or a job promotion. How you reacted and what helped you get back up after a challenge shows that it's not so much *what* happened that matters, but *what you made of it*. Once you're aware of which emotions helped you bounce back, you can tap into those emotions in tough times. Simultaneously, by recognizing those negative emotions that prevent you from growing, you can proactively manage them.

Being *resilient* is not about avoiding obstacles, disappointments or frustrations. It's about bouncing back as quickly as possible and staying in the low moments for as short a time as possible. Every opportunity to overcome an obstacle is a potential opportunity to learn and do better next time. The good news is, it's never too late. You'll continue to encounter hurdles, but by recognizing and managing the emotions they trigger, you can grow old with wise agility.

Developing a resilient mindset is like training a muscle. It can be worked on to become stronger and stronger. Managing our thoughts, feelings, and behaviors so that problems stay in perspective makes it easier to bounce back. As Dr Amit Sood, founder of the Mayo Clinic, says, "Resilience is not a trampoline, where you're down one moment and up the next. It's more like climbing a mountain without a trail map."

CHRISTINE'S JOURNEY

Christine came to us at 80, struggling to understand why she always felt guilty saying no or asking for help. She'd had enough.

Together, we discovered that as a child, she was forced to take on massive responsibilities of a household and two sisters while her parents worked. Her parents were farmers and were out in the fields most of the day. She had to assume much more than what a young girl would normally do. On a sad morning, her baby sister died in her arms while her parents went to get a doctor, further weighing on her emotions. Throughout life, both at home and work, she continued taking on so much that by 70 she suffered from stress, hypertension and ultimately a stroke.

Fortunately, this incident triggered Christine to ask for help to get rid of that heavy feeling. Through our support to strengthen her resilience, she recovered and understood the behavioral pattern which led to the grief, sadness, anger and guilt buried below her iceberg. Today, she has bounced back replacing her emotional load with calm and serenity.

Building resilience requires courage, strength, and support from others. Research shows that resilience is improved by supportive social systems. However, you need to know how to *ask* for help. Sharing your feelings to ask for support — not so that others solve your problems, but so that they help you see coping options — is a good resilience strategy. Like asking for a map to climb that mountain, eventually you'll reach the top and look back at how far you've come.

Emotional resilience will be exponentially stronger when it's accompanied by physical and intellectual resilience. Think about the emotions that emerge when you're sick, tired or bored that weaken your ability to quickly bounce back.

Resilience and dealing with disruptions are not a question of age, but of awareness and mindset.

Your life's emotional journey is a gift providing you signals and messages. Study them, learn from them and build what Oprah Winfrey calls your *emotional GPS*.

Swiss Touch: For over 300 years, Swiss people have identified emotionally with their precious watchmaking. Geography and political neutrality have allowed watchmakers to endure revolutions, wars, and depressions. Yet they almost didn't survive the 1970's quartz revolution.

Mass production reduced costs, but a deep emotional resistance to industrializing the cherished handywork of Swiss watchmakers remained. This emotional reluctance caused exports to plummet from 40 to 3 million in less than ten years.

The Swiss finally woke up and realized survival depended on embracing technology. They embraced change, innovated, bounced back and returned to center stage. Today, over half the value of watches sold globally display two words that make them the most sought-after in the world: *Swiss Made*. That's resilience!

Emotions at Work

---

*"Working hard for something we don't care about is
called stress; working hard for something we love is
called passion."* Simon Sinek

Mental health problems are one of the biggest challenges of this century. These issues show up in the workplace in the form of burnout, stress, anxiety and more.

Reports from the WHO, Deloitte, and Forbes reveal that employers play a key role in supporting the emotional well-being of their employees and that mental wellness is an absolute priority today. Emotions in the workplace play a large role in how an organization communicates within itself and to the outside world. As long as you work, they have *a real impact on you, too.*

A study by Facebook and Cornell University showed that whether face-to-face or virtually, we tend to embody the emotions we feel through our gestures, facial expressions and voice. So, at work and at home, our emotions are noticeable to others, even more when you are facing colleagues only 20 centimeters from your screen.

The consequences of emotions in the workplace have substantial impact. Positive emotions help employees attain higher levels of well-being and engagement, while negative emotions can provoke under-performance, isolation, illness and ageing. Although our emotional state profoundly influences the quality of our work, many of us are unaware of it and the impact it has. Most employers don't give emotions much attention either, preferring we leave them outside, so they don't disrupt our workday. One illustration is our client, a fifty-something menopausal woman, whose employer labeled her as 'distracted and confused' when she was simply experiencing mood swings and fatigue.

One of the most frequent emotions our aged 50+ clients express is job frustration or the feeling that something is missing in their professional life. You've likely spent one-third of your life working and there is no reason to delay doing what you really love. Acknowledging your emotions, understanding and communicating your desires *now* is crucial to working, feeling and ageing well.

In your personal life, you're allowed to react by shouting or feeling sorry for yourself. At work, however, these types of behaviors could seriously harm your reputation. Emotional balance means appropriately managing, rather than suppressing, your emotions at work. It will allow you to remain authentic, reinforce trust and enjoy better relationships.

RICHARD'S JOURNEY

Richard, 57, had been in HR for over 20 years. He had devoted time and effort and neglected his family to do his best professionally.

When he lost his job, he began dreaming about a career change he was passionate about. Despite this dream, his negative emotions of fear, insecurity and doubt held him back.

He was stuck in this mindset and 6 months later was still frustrated, lonely and jobless until a dear friend called to get him out of this tense personal and professional situation. Through our guidance, Richard networked with others who had successfully navigated similar situations. He learned to open up and express his emotions around his likes and dislikes and discovered a passion for educating autistic children — a job he still does today with joy!

Green Thumb: Eco-Emotions. Data shows that emotions influence behaviors, decision-making and consciousness that directly impact our planet. Emotional considerations such as specific moral beliefs, ecological responsibility, emotional affinity toward nature and environmental justice can be powerful predictors of sustainable behaviors. Think, for example, how indignation about waste affects decisions and behavior about consumption. How do you feel about waste of our Earth's resources?

Emotional Shake-Up Wrap-Up

This chapter has given you the equipment you need to unearth optimal emotional wellness in the years to come.

Remember:

- Emotional health is a combination of how you think, feel and the relationship you have with your deep-self and the world around you
- The first step to better manage your emotions is to increase your emotional awareness and understanding by specifically naming your emotions
- You can learn mindset, attitude and positivity exercises to tap into your *Sage* more often than your *Saboteur*
- Your heart and your brain are two important organs in dealing with your emotions. Take care to nourish them properly, inside and out
- You can learn to manage your emotions rather than be managed by them
- Resilience is essential to rebound from life's challenges. It can be learned, developed and strengthened
- Your past holds a wealth of experiences to serve as learning points toward emotional fulfilment
- Emotions have a place in everything you do, even at work
- It's never too late to increase your emotional well-being, so how do you feel about starting now?

Elevate Now!

Starting now, commit to *noticing* how you feel. As you go about your day, notice when, where and how feelings pop up, then try to observe how those feelings make you act. Remember, emotions are felt through all of your senses – sight, sound, touch, taste and smell.

Stuff we love:
- Noticing when we're feeling lonely if we actually reach out to connect with someone

- Observing when we're feeling stressed if we stand up, take a walk or shift our space
- Noticing when we're feeling frustrated if we share it with someone or if we just stew
- Journaling what we notice to keep our brain in top shape.

In the *Thrive-Guide* you will discover how to elevate from *knowing* about emotional well-being to *doing* something positive about it!

5

Intellectual

"Intellectual growth should commence at birth and only cease at death." Albert Einstein

---

Many, due to thoughts on ageing, consider older adults incapable or less willing to roll up their sleeves and learn something new. However, research proves that when it comes to learning, there's no age limit. The more engaged you remain intellectually, the more you can contribute to the world and the happier you will be.

The brain and how it works changes with age. Mental decline is one of the most feared consequences of ageing. However, such decline is preventable and there are specific ways to Gear-up for optimal brain functioning.

Your brain is like a muscle. You can keep it in shape by stimulating the growth of its cell's extensions — called dendrites. Each time you learn or practice something new, dendrites grow, and more neural pathways are created and nurtured. This mental manipulation increases activity along dendrite pathways allowing memories to stay longer. This process occurs naturally throughout childhood. However, as you grow older, it's up to *you* to provoke stimulation through continuous learning and change. In short, the more active your brain, the better your memory.

Brain activities do not only stimulate memory and connections between nerve cells, but they may also even help the brain generate *new* cells. These new cells further develop neurological *plasticity* by building up a reserve as a guard against future cell loss. That is the beauty of our body's cells, they never stop renewing themselves. Super cool!

For most, raw mental horsepower starts declining after the age of 30. However, knowledge and expertise, critical for job performance among other things, keep increasing even beyond 80.

According to *The Psychology of Retirement* by Doreen Rosenthal and Susan Moore, retirement ranks among the top-ten life's most stressful events. Though retiring from work-related stress is often a great relief and beneficial for health, losing daily structure and work relationships can also take its toll. Keeping older people active at work or in the community ensures meaningful, intellectually stimulating and purposeful lives all while maintaining relationships.

Dr. Janet Ruth Heller says, "Many people in the 55+ age group are frustrated with their jobs and are considering a new career. Many individuals in this age group also have a lot of energy and live far from their children and grandchildren or have no children." Putting energy into learning new things through education or hobbies can help keep your mind sharp and Gear you up for whatever future you choose.

Adapting to change, accepting diversity and connecting with others while mastering how to support and collaborate with them, all contribute to intellectual well-being. Beyond your personal benefits, drawing from your wealth of experience, knowledge and skills is key to shaping an intellectually inspired, creative and diverse world.

In the Blue Zones — five regions of the world where a higher than usual number of people live much longer than average — the importance of maintaining social bonds and having a sense of purpose have been identified as *critical elements* for long life.

This quick quiz will help you start thinking about your intellectual well-being. Your answers will reveal if this Dimension is ready for some shaking-up!

1. How curious are you to learn new things and acquire new skills?
2. How easily and happily do you adjust to change?
3. How satisfied are you with your connections and relationships?

Your Real Brain Teaser

"No brain is stronger than its weakest think." Thomas L. Masson

Challenging your brain with mental exercises helps stimulate and maintain its cells, keeping it young. That's building brain muscles. Any mentally stimulating activity like learning new skills, getting a new job, or volunteering builds up and boosts brain power. In fact, anything requiring manual dexterity and mental effort such as puzzles, math or crafts are amazing brain enhancers.

Did you know that the more senses you use in learning, the more brain mass is exercised in retaining it? So, venturing into the unfamiliar, such as visiting a new museum and opting for the audio-guide to enhance your observing, challenges multiple, enriching your brain's experience. Training your brain to adapt to change, new habits and unplanned events contribute to its overall fitness. There is no need to go for big changes. Small daily habit changes such as brushing your teeth with the opposite hand or taking another route to buy groceries, will help ensure lifelong brain flexibility.

Everyone has the occasional mental lapse forgetting or losing something. Memory lapses can occur at any age but ageing alone is *not* the cause of intellectual decline. Studies show that you can help prevent intellectual decline and reduce the risk of dementia with some basic habits for getting and keeping your mind alive and well. Staying mentally and physically fit will make you feel better, and help you thrive independently for longer.

Training your brain to adapt to change, new habits and unplanned events contribute to your brain's fitness. There is no need to go for big changes, small daily habit changes such as brushing your teeth with the opposite hand, will help ensure lifelong brain flexibility. Go for baby steps because each incremental step will facilitate the next. Think of a deep snow-covered path. The first step through is challenging while each successive step clears the passage.

Research shows that physical activity also works out your mind. Animals that exercise regularly increase the number of blood vessels carrying oxygen-rich blood to the region of the brain responsible for reaction. Exercise also spurs the development of new nerve cells and increases connections between brain cells. This results in a brain that is more efficient and adaptive which, in turn, translates into better performance. Physical activity also lowers blood pressure, improves cholesterol levels, balances blood sugar and reduces mental stress which all support brain *and* heart health.

Good nutrition can nourish your mind as well as your body. Extensive research shows that certain foods which are particularly rich in healthful components like omega-3 fatty acids, B vitamins, and antioxidants, support and boost brain health and mental function. These components are a significant part of the Mediterranean style diet which has been proven to decrease cognitive impairment and dementia in adults.

By stimulating your brain intellectually *and* taking care of your physical Dimension, you are doubly *Gearing-up* for a youthful brain!

Swiss Touch: Did you know that the Swiss created Velcro, cellophane, the Swiss Army Knife, the potato peeler, Helvetica font and milk chocolate, just to name a few? According to the Global Innovation Index, Switzerland has shown up as the most innovative country in the world for ten consecutive years, outperforming other European Union countries in all areas. This proves that despite — or thanks to — having practically no natural resources, you can always use brain power to innovate and come out on top.

Fire to Wire

Donald Hebb, a neuropsychologist, first used the phrase, 'Thoughts that fire together wire together...' in 1949. He described how pathways in the brain are formed and reinforced through repetition. The more the brain does a specific task, the stronger that neural network becomes, making the thought process more efficient each successive time. Ingrained habits are the best example. How easy is it to drive your car or tie your laces by the age of 50?

Dr Joe Dispenza, thought leader driven by the conviction that each of us has the potential for greatness, has explored the science behind the power of our thoughts and how we can use them to create — or re-create — our life. According to Dr Joe, thanks to the wiring and firing of thoughts, "All creation begins with a thought and the best way to predict our future is to create it."

Once you start thinking about and envisioning your future, your brain fires in new sequences, patterns, and combinations. As soon as you see that vision, the thoughts in your mind become that experience. Then you begin to feel the emotions associated with the future before they actually happen. If you keep thinking about making that future a reality, you begin to insert yourself into the future scenario and your brain begins to change. When you're truly focused and pay attention with all your senses, there comes a moment when your brain doesn't know the difference between reality and imagination anymore. In fact, the thoughts you *feel* will become like a real-life experience in your mind.

So, when you change your thoughts, you change your brain, and when you change your brain, you change your *mind*. Isn't this a cool thought to be able to reprogram your mind, and subsequently your behaviors and life, at any age?

Change is about unlearning certain behaviors and relearning new ones. It's about reinventing yourself. Every time you learn something new, you forge a new synaptic connection in your thinking brain. It's not enough to just learn that information. It's important to take what you learned and apply it, personalize it, demonstrate it to change something about yourself. When you do, you have acquired a new experience. New experiences enhance the brain through our five senses. Once you capture something intellectually, your five senses contribute by chemically triggering emotions related to your intellectual experience. This is another example of how your Emotional Dimension and Intellectual Dimension function together.

Stage Your Change

"Change the way you look at things and the things you look at change." Wayne W. Dyer

---

The need for change is constant as we strive to live healthful, productive lives. Ageing often triggers the necessity to make significant lifestyle modifications, from relocating or developing new social networks, to taking new medications. For younger adults, changing health behaviors lacks a sense of urgency since the negative effects from unhealthy lifestyles may not show up for many years. As you grow older, however, the consequences of unhealthy behaviors catch up with you and are often immediate and potentially life threatening.

The National Academy of Science suggests that although older adults may be less likely to initiate behavioral changes, we are more likely to maintain any changes we *do* make. This may be due to the powerful link between mature emotions and decisions.

How well do *you* adapt to change?

The *change curve* derived from the work of Elisabeth Kubler-Ross, describes the internal emotional journey that individuals experience when dealing with change and transition. This journey consists of five stages: *Shock and Denial; Anger; Bargaining; Depression and Acceptance.*

Let's explore each with an example everyone will understand:

Shock and denial: After the initial shock of being confronted with a change, we often resist engaging with it, almost trying to prove that it's unreal or unnecessary.

***

Covid19 is just another flu!

***

Anger: Then, there comes a point at which we can no longer deny. Anger or blame show up.

> *It's not fair! This stupid virus is going to make me miss out on…*

***

Bargaining: Next, elements of bargaining often emerge. Mood and performance adjust to reality as you realize the impact these changes will have on you.

> *I guess I had better adjust some minor stuff like working from home, purchasing online and watching out for the elderly. So annoying. I hope it won't last long.*

***

Depression: The downward curve to this point has been illustrated by your drive to hold on to or revert to the old situation. Energy, morale and performance may fluctuate, while confusion, sadness, or even depression start to show up.

> *2020 is an awful year! This cannot really be happening, I'm not sure I can cope with confinements and quarantines much longer.*

***

Acceptance: Finally, you hit a point where you accept at a deeper level that change must happen and you resolve to face the *new normal*. Only at this point can you begin to open up and look to explore new, positive possibilities and integrate these into your new way of being.

I'm grateful to be well and can protect myself by wearing a mask, practicing physical distancing and limiting my physical interactions. I wonder how I might help...

***

We hope that this example resonates with you and that it allows you to look at life's inevitable changes through a different lens. By understanding these stages, you can anticipate change with more agility. The good news is, thanks to better emotional control, stability and more effective coping strategies that come with age, your ability to adapt increases over the course of lifetime.

Change is inevitable. How you deal with it depends on your belief in your ability to succeed, which is called *self-efficacy*. Self-efficacy has long been known to play a critical role in self-regulation and self-motivation. It links your beliefs with your goals, effort, and perseverance while coping with change.

Think about a major life change you have experienced. Do you recognize your stages of change? How did you manage them? Where did you succeed and where did you get stuck? Use this observation and recognition to determine how well you're Geared-up for the path before you. By the way, a great variety of emerging evidence suggests that social support is critical for successful adaptation to change.

A Word on Books

"The more that you read, the more things you will know. The more that you learn, the more places you'll go." Dr. Seuss

Being well-read and inquisitive are traits that we often downplay in youth because we fear we may be called a nerd or uncool. However, with maturity, we understand the significance and value of certain traits, and in this case, it's being well-read.

Staying cool means being in the know and the only way to know about things is to read. This includes understanding current events, politics, fashion, music, sports, dance, the arts and so on.

Reading books keeps your mind engaged as you grow older and has been shown to help prevent disorders such as Alzheimer's and dementia. The earlier you start, the better. People who've engaged in mentally stimulating activities all their lives are less likely to develop the plaques, lesions, and other brain deficiencies linked with dementia. Seniors who read and solve math problems daily maintain and improve their cognitive functioning.

People who read books for 30 minutes a day have been shown to live longer than those who didn't read at all. On average, book readers live for almost two years longer than non-readers. That's definitely *not* uncool.

Reading increases vocabulary, comprehension, memory, dreaming and visualizing. It helps reduce stress, depression, heart rate and blood pressure. Reading stimulates empathy — the ability to understand and share the feelings of another. This all sharpens your intellectual Gear while simultaneously calibrating your emotional and physical Gears.

Any and all reading provides the advantages described above. So, all forms of books — e-books, paper books, readers or audio books — are wonderful. Research indicates, however, that reading *physical* books has added benefits. People who read *print* books score higher on comprehension tests and remember more of what they read than people who read the same material digitally. This might be because people tend to read print more slowly than digital content. In whatever format you choose, it's never too late (or early) to read, read, read...

MARTHA'S JOURNEY

At 63, approaching retirement and widowed, Martha felt a desire to do something new. Though she was in excellent physical health, she lacked a sense of purpose and felt lonely.

After exploring her talents and passions, she decided to create a book club. She now organizes monthly gatherings to learn and exchange opinions on books before enjoying wine and social time. She discovered a true love and enthusiasm for the intellectual stimulation from reading, has a busy new social life and is proud of her book club.

Your Digital Divide

"Digital technology is the same revolution as adding sound to pictures and the same revolution as adding color to pictures. Nothing more and nothing less." George Lucas

In today's digital world, we're all expected to use the internet for everything from e-finance to telehealth. Due to the overwhelming presence of Information and Communication Technologies (ICT) in modern society, digital literacy has evolved exponentially — from an option into a need. This means that technological skills are essential to maintaining digital literacy as you age.

There is a growing gap between the tools used by the younger and the ageing populations. According to Internet World Stats, after screening 3.6 billion people worldwide, 48.3% don't have access to technology. This disparity regarding internet and ICT usage and availability is commonly referred to as a digital divide.

To conquer your digital divide, it's more important than ever to stay up to date with technology. Evidence shows that older adults readily adopt and learn new technologies when they are relevant to their important life goals. In other words, you learn best when you learn for a purpose and not just learning for the sake of it.

How's your digital literacy?

76

CECILIA'S JOURNEY

Cecilia, 57, had never touched a computer in her life and had no desire to do so. She felt fulfilled dedicating herself to her family, home and neighbors; until the day her son relocated to another continent.

Fearful of losing contact with him, she tapped into the social media addictions of her eight grandchildren. In a matter of weeks, she became an expert in WhatsApp, and Facebook.

Today, Cecilia is quicker than the kids on her iPad, she's revamped relationships with her family, re-kindled long-lost friendships, made new ones and continues to impress everyone with her cool tech-savvy.

Time to Play

> *"We don't stop playing because we grow old; we grow old because we stop playing."* George Bernard Shaw

Did you know that in the United States there is a National Institute for Play? This is for a good reason. Play brings joy and offers some real ageing benefits for both you and others.

However, somewhere between childhood and adulthood, we stopped playing. Society tends to dismiss play for adults, perceiving it as an unproductive or even a guilty pleasure. We often feel that once we reach adulthood, we must behave. Besides, we're busy and there's no time for play! Seriously?!

Well, for optimal ageing, it may be worth giving yourself permission to play. In fact, play is important for all Dimensions of well-being. It's also very, very cool. Research suggests that playfulness in later life improves cognitive, emotional, social, psychological functioning and healthy ageing overall.

Play helps us connect and stay sharp, maintain memory and thinking skills. Having fun makes learning easier, at any age. In addition, sharing laughter and fun with others fosters relationships through empathy, trust, and intimacy. Fun triggers the release of endorphins, the body's natural feel-good chemicals, which promote an overall sense of well-being, relieves stress and can even alleviate pain.

According to the American Journal of Play (it's real!), there exists a measure of adult playfulness: The Adult Playfulness Scale. The thirty-two items on the scale reflect five factors: spontaneity, expressiveness, fun, creativity, and silliness. Doesn't that sound amusing?

Playfulness can be described as relaxation, enthusiasm, being positive, optimistic and naughty. Research shows that playful adults are:

- Psychologically upbeat, happy, optimistic, cheerful, joyful, positive, relaxed, and enthusiastic
- Cognitively spontaneous, creative and whimsical
- Amusing, observably funny and humorous, which in turn solicits positive responses from others
- Behaviorally impish: acting in mischievous, naughty, clowning, and teasing ways.

Dr. Brown, the founder of the National Institute for Play, has reviewed over 6,000 *play histories*, exploring the role of play in each person's life. He found out that lack of play was just as important as other factors in predicting criminal behavior. He also found that playing together helped couples rekindle relationships. Play can even facilitate deep connections between strangers and cultivate healing. Let's face it, play deprivation — tedious and boring — is just no fun!

You need play to be healthy and the goal of *having more fun* is just as important as other adult-sounding goals. After all, what's the point of being in great shape or having more money if you're not enjoying yourself?

The most important thing is to decide what play *means* for you. As an adult, you may not even remember what you like to do. Maybe you've outgrown the things that you enjoyed in the past and haven't gotten around to identifying new ones yet.

Play could be simply fooling around with friends or colleagues, throwing a ball, building a snowman, playing with a dog, or going for a bike ride. There need not be any purpose beyond pure pleasure. By giving yourself permission to play with the joyful abandon of childhood, you can reap health benefits throughout life.

Whatever you choose, the more you play as you age, the happier and smarter you'll become.

The Connection Game

> *"Count your age by friends, not years. Count your life by smiles, not tears."* John Lennon

The quantity and quality of social relationships have powerful effects on health across your lifespan. Good social relationships can improve blood pressure, physical activity, obesity, executive function, memory, cognitive decline and life expectancy. Over 148 studies found a 50% increase in survival of people with robust social relationships, regardless of age, gender, ethnicity, or how such relationships were defined. Wow!

Satisfaction with relationships increases with age and what we tell ourselves about our relationships is just as important as the number of people in our networks. It appears your *perceptions* of social support are more powerful predictors of well-being than the actual amount of support. For example, those who *view* friends and families as supportive, report a greater sense of meaning in life and a stronger sense of purpose.

Not all relationships are equal, so health benefits vary across types of relationship. Marriage and intimate partnerships along with close friendships generally offer the most protective functions to health through companionship, emotional support and practical assistance. The benefits of camaraderie and enjoyable interaction enhance mood, support resilience, alleviate stress, and stimulate your sense of self-worth. This mood enhancement happens in our brain, likely through our hypothalamic pituitary adrenal axis, which stimulates production of our stress hormone, cortisol.

The famous Study of Adult Development at Harvard Medical School lasted over 75 years and has been one of the most extensive longitudinal studies ever. The most important message from this study is what Robert J. Waldinger, Head of the Study, often quotes, "The lessons aren't about wealth or fame or working harder and harder. The clearest message that we get from this 75-year study is this: good relationships keep us happier and healthier. Period. "

Green Thumb: Ecological Intelligence. Given today's ecological threats, there is an urgent need to re-sensitize ourselves to our ecological niche to preserve our planet, named *Ecological Intelligence (EI).* Many in science claim that EI is one of the most important forms of intelligence in our present world. Ecological Intelligence is about applying what we learn about how human activity impacts ecosystems to do less harm and live sustainably on our planet. This essential and crucial shift toward greater Ecological Intelligence will drive global changes in commerce and industry as well as in individual actions and behaviors.

On EI, Dan Goleman further states, "...while we're in school it seems that the only intelligence that counts is the academic sort... but as you live your life, it's clear that there are other abilities that matter immensely, for personal happiness, for relationships, for success, for teamwork, for leadership."

Intellectual Shake-Up Wrap-Up

In this chapter, you have learned that mental decline is not inevitable and there are specific ways to Gear-up for sustainable brain function.

- By stimulating your brain intellectually, it stays flexible
- Nutrition and physical activity enhance brain health
- The best way to predict your future is to create it
- Reading — especially printed books — increases longevity and happiness
- Digital literacy is no longer a nice to have, but a necessity to be and feel included in modern society
- Change is inevitable and how you deal with it depends on your belief in your own ability to succeed — your self-efficacy
- Play brings joy and offers some real fun ageing benefits for you and others
- Social connections, companionship and emotional support are key to longevity and happiness.

Elevate Now!

Starting now, *change* some normal everyday routines to stimulate your brain.

Stuff we love to change:

- Brush your hair or teeth with the opposite hand
- Take a different walk or drive
- Dare to make a mistake because your brain grows more when you fail and learn from that failure!
- With whom you hang out, to transform ideas, conversations, and inspiration.

Want to stay a SMART cookie? Your *Thrive-Guide* is a fun source of games, ideas, tips and resources for your intellectual workout!

6

Spiritual

"It's not enough to have lived. We should be determined to live for something." Winston Churchill

---

The Oxford English Dictionary defines spirituality as *the quality of being concerned with the human spirit or soul as opposed to material or physical things.* Our *Non-Material Equipment* mentioned earlier in our book.

Each person sees spirituality differently. For some, it's about believing in an organized religion. For others, it's about non-religious experiences that help them connect with their inner selves through reflection, time in nature, prayer, yoga, gratitude or other personal practice.

Today, the percentage of adults who identify themselves as religious in most industrialized countries is declining, while it remains generally high in non-industrialized nations. However, humans everywhere might be pursuing spirituality more than ever. Meditation has tripled in popularity since 2012, mostly among adults aged 45-64. As for the 5000-year-old practice of yoga, the number of yogis has increased by over 50% in the US and 413% in Japan in the same time frame.

Summaries by the Mayo Clinic of over 1000 studies showed improved outcomes in physical and mental health for older adults who value spirituality. People that consider themselves spiritual literally live longer!

Improved self-esteem, strengthened relationships, increased compassion and a positive outlook on life have all been shown as specific benefits of spirituality. Avoiding spirituality has been linked to depression and unhappiness. Definitely worth contemplating, right?

Spiritual individuals strive toward a better life and consider personal growth and fulfillment an *intention* of life. Likely, if you're reading this book, this resonates with you, continuously focusing on aligning with what deeply matters to you.

This quick quiz will help you start thinking about your spiritual well-being. Your answers will reveal if this Dimension is ready for some shaking-up!

1. How good are you at accepting events and others as they are, without judgement?
2. How do you define your sense of connectedness with creation and all other living beings?
3. How consistent with your values is your everyday life — including your job?

Why Now?

> *"The fact is you already know how to find yourself;*
> *you have just gotten distracted and disoriented. Once*
> *refocused, you will realize that you not only have the*
> *ability to find yourself, you have the ability to free*
> *yourself. Whether you choose to do so or not is entirely*
> *up to you."* Michael Singer

Up through your 40s you were likely swept into a whirlwind of expectations and pressure to deliver and succeed. Your responsibilities at work and at home grew as you built your life, home, family, and career, doing all the *stuff that needed to get done.*

By 50, you've likely experienced tough life events such as distressed friends or family, divorce, financial loss, death. You know that life is not always gentle. These events, though painful, often trigger the understanding of what really matters in life. The realization that running around to *get stuff done* may not be the only, nor the best way to live. As you get older with fewer years ahead, you likely focus more on the present. You likely prioritize what you *do* have, rather than anticipating the future you might have.

The later part of life presents an ideal opportunity to unravel purpose and meaning in yourself and in your life. To realign with *you*. Not you, the parent, the professional, the spouse, but you as an individual. It's like pressing the pause button on your previous years to find that sweet spot of an active, meaningful life. Not just *running but shifting from busy-ness to aware-ness.*

Research shows that spirituality — religious or not — is seen by adults as a positive force that helps:

• Face life with more resilience and hope
• Improve relationships
• Cope with stressors such as financial or health concerns.

Happiness research shows there are three things that make people happy: close relationships; a job or pastime they love; and helping others. Money and material things do not have a lot to do with happiness, and people who emphasize them have been shown to be less happy than those who don't. The coolest thing is, happiness is free.

In 50+ years you've likely explored and travelled to many places. Now is the ideal time to take a journey inside yourself to connect with your heart and soul and elevate your ageing. Remember, the trail you leave behind will be your legacy.

We invite you to contemplate these questions as you heighten your spiritual future. Your answers will reveal if this Dimension is ready for some shaking-up. If not now, when?

• What do I truly believe in and value?
• What is my real purpose, my mission?
• What legacy do I want to leave?

Believe in Values

"If you change the belief first, changing the action is easier." Peter McWilliams

---

We use both *beliefs and values* to guide our behavior and to form our attitudes, yet beliefs and values are quite different.

In the article, *The Biochemistry of Beliefs*, *beliefs* are described as the guiding principles in life that provide direction and meaning. Beliefs are the preset, organized filters of how you see the world. In their absence, or your inability to tap into them, you feel powerless.

Beliefs originate from everything you hear and experience from the day you are born. Scientifically, beliefs are developed as stimuli received and stored as reliable information in your memory. They are critical for your judgment and decision-making.

Beliefs are the convictions you hold to be true, without actual proof or evidence. They are assumptions that you make about the world and your values stem from them.

Beliefs could include ideas such as *all people are created equal*, which would guide us to treat everyone equally. Conversely you might believe that *all people are not created equal*, which could result in prejudiced or biased behaviors. You have the power to choose your beliefs and resulting behaviors.

Your beliefs grow from what you see, hear, experience, read and think. They come in many shapes and sizes, from the trivial and the easily verified — I believe it will rain today — to profound leaps of faith — I believe in God. Taken together they form your personal guidebook to reality, telling you not just what is factually correct, but also what's right and wrong. This makes beliefs, arguably, both the most fundamental and important function of your brain.

Let's rev up your Gears again. Have you thought about your perception about money lately? Your beliefs about nutrition or sleep? What about your convictions about yourself and your capabilities to face the years

86

to come? Your beliefs are interconnected and interdependent. What you believe in one Dimension will influence the others, which in turn affect how you age — believe it or not!

Your values represent the principles or standards of your behavior. Your judgement of what is important in life.

Everyone has an internal system of beliefs and values. Equality, honesty, effort, perseverance, ecology and so many more. By the time you're 50, your beliefs and values have been wired as you've accumulated evidence and experiences to support or challenge your personal system.

Aligning your life decisions and your core values produces satisfaction, a sense of happiness and fulfilment. A misalignment can cause everything from minor problems to major disruptions. As Brian Tracy puts it, "Just as your car runs more smoothly and requires less energy to go faster and farther when the wheels are in perfect alignment, you perform better when your thoughts, feelings, emotions, goals, and values are in balance."

You use your values to steer toward what's important to *you*. Values evolve throughout life and like the wheels of a car or the Gears of a watch, need realigning regularly.

Spirituality, beliefs and values have been found to be a source of strength, comfort and hope and bring about a sense of community and belonging, especially in difficult times. Despite the challenges of ageing, spirituality — in any form — helps older adults live a more positive and meaningful life.

So, when was the last time you realigned with your spirituality, beliefs and values?

***

"Your beliefs become your thoughts
Your thoughts become your words
Your words become your actions
Your actions become your habits
Your habits become your values
Your values become your destiny."
Mahatma Gandhi

***

Green Thumb: Spiritual ecology is an emerging field, and its principles are simple: To resolve environmental issues such as depletion of species, global warming, and over-consumption, we must examine and reassess our *beliefs* about the Earth, and our responsibilities toward the welfare of the planet. Spiritual Ecology asserts a need for conservation work to use contemporary religion and spirituality to raise awareness of and engagement in ecological issues.

Gratitude Attitude

"Feeling gratitude and not expressing it is like wrapping a present and not giving it." William Arthur Ward

Gratitude is considered by many to be the ultimate spiritual practice. The word itself comes from the Proto-Indo-European root, *gwere*, meaning *to praise, to celebrate; to be in contact with the Divine.* In other words, being grateful is equivalent to feeling the presence of the Divine — a state of personal bliss.

Gratitude is appreciation for what we receive, tangible or intangible. It helps us focus on what we have instead of what we don't and to acknowledge the goodness in our lives. In the process, we usually recognize that the source of that goodness lies partially outside ourselves. As a result, gratitude helps you connect to something greater than you — other people, nature, or a higher power — your spirituality.

Science provides solid proof supporting what many religions and spiritual traditions have been preaching for ages: gratitude *does* good.

Neuroscientists assert that gratitude boosts the neurotransmitters, dopamine and serotonin, and the hormone oxytocin, all associated with well-being and a positive outlook. The prominent Dr. Deepak Chopra references clinical studies that prove the positive effects of gratitude on the recovery of patients with heart failure and many other ailments.

In positive psychology research, gratitude is strongly and consistently associated with greater happiness. Gratitude helps you feel more positive emotions and relish good experiences while improving relationships, health and your capacity to deal with adversity.

Researchers are beginning to unravel the biological and developmental foundations of gratitude, and they're finding reason to believe it may be easier to feel grateful and express gratitude as we grow older.

Neuroscientists have suggested that older people have a brighter outlook because the limbic system — specifically the amygdala, that area of the brain responsible for emotional attention and memory, remember? — shrinks in response to negative information. Positive information, on the other hand, increases limbic response.

Do you think there might be a gap between how you express gratitude and how it's perceived? Adrian Gostick and Chester Elton, in Leading with Gratitude, conclude that people are less likely to express gratitude at work than anywhere else. Their research shows that 67% of bosses believe they're good at appreciating work while 87% of their employees believe they're not. This flagrant workplace *gratitude gap* has been shown to further extend itself to home and family. Think: parents versus kids, or husband versus wife, rather than employers versus employees.

In light of the huge potential payoffs on mental, emotional and physical well-being, gratitude is worth practicing and developing.

Think About Mindfulness and Meditation

"The next time you sit down to meditate, practice yoga or any other alternative activity, just remember, you might actually be changing your life." Dr Joe Dispenza

---

If you think this topic is *woo-woo*, you should definitely read on!

According to Mindful.org, mindfulness is *the basic human ability to be fully present, aware of where we are and what we're doing, and not overly reactive or overwhelmed by what's going on around us.* Every human being possesses the capacity to practice mindfulness, and it does not need to be learned. However, we often need to learn or re-learn how to access and develop it.

Evidence suggests that mindfulness can promote cognitive, emotional and physical well-being while reducing emotional distress, especially in older adults.

Some confuse *Mindfulness* with *Meditation*. Think of Mindfulness as the awareness of *some-thing*, and Meditation as the awareness of *no-thing*. You can practice Mindfulness anytime, anywhere. All you need to do is simply show up fully engaged in the here and now. Mindfulness releases *happy* chemicals in the brain, lowers blood pressure, improves digestion, reduces tension and pain.

Mindfulness is a powerful tool that creates time to pause between your actions and reactions. This pause allows you to develop Emotional Intelligence by slowing down your *automatic pilot* bringing awareness to what's happening. Mindfulness provokes thought before action.

These three daily practices can help you see just how simple, yet impactful, mindfulness can be:

1. *Mindful eating*: A pause before you eat to ask yourself if you're really hungry, and how hungry you are, can give you the space to eat

with more intention and attention. This simple practice can increase pleasure and even prevent overeating.

2. *Mindful movement:* A pause before you start any physical activity gives you the opportunity to choose which activity really serves you best right now. This mindful moment can help avoid fatigue-related injuries while connecting you with your true needs. Maybe you'll realize sleep is more useful than a workout just now.

3. *Mindful response*: A pause to stop and think before lashing out on family or co-workers, can allow your brain the time to respond thoughtfully. Reacting harshly might end in regret and do more harm than good.

See, nobody is suggesting you sit like a monk for hours in some strange posture without moving an eyelid!

Some evidence-based benefits of mindfulness include:

• Improved memory and social interaction
• Enhanced sleep, attention and concentration
• Reduced stress, anxiety and addictions
• More self-awareness and self-esteem
• Improved immunity, blood pressure and pain management.

While Mindfulness can be applied to any situation and for any length of time, Meditation is usually practiced for a specific amount of time. There are many forms of meditation and techniques that can help cultivate it. Some aim to develop a clear and focused mind, others a loving kindness, compassion or forgiveness. Using the body as a means to develop awareness, such as walking, is yet another form of meditation.

The purpose of Meditation is to slow down your brain waves to go be-yond your thinking, conscious mind. It's about relaxing your entire be-ing, like falling asleep, while keeping your mind awake. Through medi-tation, you can access your subconscious. Very cool indeed.

Your subconscious is your brain's operating system. By accessing it, you can alter habits, behaviors and remove emotional scars or simply open yourself up to the realm of the unknown and the spiritual.

While meditating, you're not awake, nor sleeping, nor dreaming. You're in the transcendental state, an experience that elevates you beyond time and space, and makes you feel one with the universe. For thousands of years, poets, philosophers, and spiritualists have tried to attain or describe this state of oneness which today remains objectively inexplicable.

Meditation improves physical and psychological states, including energy, motivation, and strength. Beyond these improvements, scientists consider meditation a solution to many lifestyle issues. Extensive evidence shows how meditation can rewire neural channels to promote inner peace and balance. Some scientifically proven meditation benefits include managing your *monkey mind* and focus, feeling more insightful, empathetic and self-compassionate and regulating emotions, sensations of pain, hunger and thirst.

Meditation is a gateway to awareness and expansion into the future. It allows you to connect now to the future you want.

Relaxing your body yet staying conscious is a skill to develop. With meditation, like with any exercise, the more you practice, the better you get. Just as if you were training to get in shape, any time spent meditating is better than none. So why not begin developing your brain now so that you have more raw materials to create, dream, learn, and improve your future?

SYLVIA'S JOURNEY

After attending a 5-day Living Well Retreat with Ellen, Sylvia, 55, experienced professional guided meditation for the first time. Sylvia said, "Since that retreat five years ago, I've literally thought of those guided meditation moments every day of my life. Sometimes they pop up during my yoga practice, sometimes while sitting at a red light or while swimming or even falling asleep. I instantly rediscover the state of calm I discovered during the retreat and function better for the rest of my day. I highly recommend experiencing formal meditation to every one of every age. The positive benefits are indescribable."

Latest Posture on Yoga

> *"Yoga is not a work-out, it is a work-in...this is the point of (a) spiritual practice; to make us teachable, to open up our hearts, and focus our awareness..."* Rolf Gates

Gentlemen, please don't stop reading here, this is more for you than you may believe!

Yogi is technically male, and Yogini is the term used for female practitioners. There are about 300 million people who practice yoga in the world. Almost 30% of yogis in the US are male and almost 14 million are over the age of 50. There is a good reason for this; let's discover why.

The true purpose of the ancient tradition of yoga was spiritual development to train the body and mind to self-observe and become aware of their own nature. Yoga cultivates discernment, awareness, self-regulation and higher consciousness. With yoga's growing popularity in recent years, more people have turned to yoga seeking physical rather than spiritual development. Some argue that this has disconnected the practitioner from the ancient inner experience.

In the words of Paramahansa Yogananda, "Many people think of yoga as just physical exercises, the asanas or postures that have gained widespread popularity in recent decades, but these are actually only the most superficial aspects of this profound science of unfolding the infinite potential of the human mind and soul."

Yoga could be your means to aligning your infinite potential with something deeper. Studies show that yoga may be able to help slow down the ageing process. It improves bone density, coordination and balance, which help to eliminate the most common cause of fractures and falls so common with age. Yoga improves posture, range of motion, flexibility, strength, anxiety, and walking pace. Obviously, none of those crooked old folks you're thinking of are yogis or yoginis!

Weekly yoga practice can bolster brain activity, improve memory and stress management and delay cognitive decline. When done regularly, it can be just as effective as memory enhancement training to help avoid the brain-related pitfalls of ageing. According to the mindfulness educator, B. Grace Bullock, this is thanks to yoga's integration of movement with breath awareness and focused attention which facilitates neural communication between brain and body.

Multiple studies suggest that yoga also has positive effects on stress and inflammation related to biological ageing. These effects were observed on heart disease, stroke and diabetes as well as brain neuroplasticity and Alzheimer's.

As we age, our rib cage elevates, our ribs become more horizontal, and the diaphragm stiffens. So, as we grow older, we need more effort to exhale and inhale fully. Mere minutes of yoga increases our breathing capacity.

The great news? Only two to three hours of yoga per week can improve your health and, unlike most physical activities, yoga has *no* age limit.

So, are you guys finally convinced? Good. Now take a deep breath in and exhale.

Look Forward to Leave Behind

"What you leave behind is not what is engraved in stone monuments, but what is woven in the lives of others." Pericles

Have you ever wondered how your presence on Earth has impacted others? How has what you've done, decided, or said contributed to or inspired people?

For many people over 50, the legacy they will leave really matters. What can feel futile seems to make sense as you become clearer on your legacy. Aligning your life to this legacy goes further than leaving assets to children or friends. Leaving a legacy means impressing a hallmark on the life of others.

Your legacy will touch those you know well, those who have crossed your life at a certain point, as well as others you have somehow inspired or impacted. Were you ever astonished when somebody told you that you influenced them deeply when you had no idea of that? Maybe you didn't even know the person? Leaving an imprint on lives is stimulating, reassuring and moving. It means that you and your life mattered.

Once you are clear and aligned with what you feel is important to leave behind, you can start building your legacy. You can begin living and acting in a way that you want others to remember, starting today.

Aligning with your personal legacy will influence your day-to-day life and decisions about what is really important. In today's digital world, it's easy and fast to share your values, actions and opinions. Why not be the role model you desire with authenticity, passion, benevolence and enthusiasm?

Leaving a legacy is your personal branding. It will last forever, so choose it wisely, with thought and love. Like dear friends, *quality* time and memories outweigh *quantity*. You matter much more than you may think.

BILL'S JOURNEY

Successful careers behind him, stable marriage, grown kids and grand-kids, Bill lived an intense and busy life. At 56, his best friend suddenly died, and Bill realized that he'd taken life for granted. His notion of time, purpose and legacy became urgent. We helped him reconnect with his belief in loyalty, his value of authenticity and purpose to impact others so that he would make the best of his life. He found balance, serenity and focus, and expressed feeling reconnected with something bigger than himself. He discovered an inner happiness and fulfillment he'd forgotten during his hectic life.

Spiritual Shake-Up Wrap-Up

This time of your life presents an ideal opportunity to tap into your purpose and meaning, your spirituality — however you define it.

- Spirituality shows up differently for each of us
- With spirituality at the core of your values, your physical, emotional and mental health will improve, and you may live longer
- Evidence shows a direct link between spirituality and happiness
- Gratitude may be the ultimate spiritual practice. It's free, cultivable and makes everybody feel great
- Mindfulness can be applied to any situation throughout the day and is the best-known way to reconnect with your spiritual self
- Meditation and yoga are gateways to awareness to help slow the ageing process through ancient mind-body connection
- Choosing your legacy now is key to your purpose
- Social relationships improve health and long life.

Elevate Now!

Starting now, *pause* and take a deep breath — standing if possible — every hour. Taking just those few seconds to breathe allows you to reconnect and realign with *you*. It will also relax, calm, improve focus, relieve tension, and can give you new perspective.

When we love to pause and breathe:

- When beginning a difficult conversation
- Before eating and somewhere mid-meal
- Prepping for public speaking, webinars, or meetings — as a group or team
- Every time you see a reminder (a post-it, push notification or other) to *just breathe.*

The *Thrive-Guide* provides valuable inspiration to elevate your spiritual self — mind, body and attitude.

7

Financial

"Make sure you have a plan for your life in your hand, and that includes the financial plan and your mission." Manoj

---

The world's greatest financial worry is retirement.

According to a study by Zurich Insurance Group and Smith School at Oxford University, 44% of us are worried about money upon retirement. For the 55-70 age-group, this figure jumps to 59%. Over half of these concerns relate to not having enough money for retirement and the inability to pay medical costs.

This chapter will *not* focus on financial recommendations or advice because this is too specific to each person, culture and circumstances. Rethinking one's financial mindset is, however, universal. We *will*, therefore, focus on recalibrating your approach to finances. We'll show you how and why your mindset, relationship and values around money *really* matter. You'll discover why financial planning and upskilling are particularly critical now.

Financial wellness is not about how much money you have, but about how you *choose* to manage it. Money management affects every aspect of your life including your emotional and physical wellness. Imagine no money worries but loneliness, depression or constant physical pain. A *financially well* person is someone who is as equipped as possible and consequently least anxious about finances.

Financial wellness is about building healthy financial habits and aligning them with what matters most to you. You're likely at a crossroads of your life now, between major life events, such as children leaving home, parents departing and job transition. Your priorities may shift as income and expenses change. When worry and uncertainty dominate your thoughts, your relationships, security and well-being are all at risk. Now is the perfect time to overhaul your finances and your *mindset about money.*

Just think about it. You have another 20-30 years to live and thrive beyond retirement age. Financial security includes your ability to manage commitments, meet financial goals and protect against older-age risks. Due to the stressful nature of this Dimension, specific professional financial planning must be anticipated well-ahead of transition time to manage potential challenges before they arise. Financial advisors, consultants and experts are readily accessible for every situation. It's up to you to choose one that fits.

The following quick quiz will reveal if your Financial Dimension is ready for some shaking-up.

1. How confident do you feel about your current and future financial situation?
2. Have you thought about what will happen when (or if) you and/or your partner retire?
3. What skills do you have to plan your financial future?

It's All Relative

Up to 90% of the decisions we make are unconscious. Remember the iceberg metaphor? By plunging below the iceberg (unconscious) and surfacing above it (conscious), you can take charge of your decisions.

To enjoy a cool lifestyle free of financial stress, you must have a healthy relationship with money.

This healthy relationship comes through building the unique set of beliefs and attitudes that drive your decisions about spending and handling money. Let's call it your *money mindset.*

If your money mindset is built on negative statements such as 'I'm terrible with money', 'I'll never be well-off' or 'Money's a dirty word', you may be neglecting saving.

People who have a positive money mindset believe things like:

- I have the freedom to spend, but I can also say no
- I don't determine my worth by comparing myself to others
- It's possible to achieve my financial goals.

To better understand your relationship with money and coming to terms with your finances, it's worth asking yourself whether you have a positive or negative money mindset and how you feel about that.

Your money mindset is tremendously influenced by *past* experiences. Thinking about how money was handled during your youth can help you understand the foundation of your beliefs. If you're in a relationship, this awareness can also help you get to the root of discussions you and your partner may have about money. Their experiences were probably totally different than yours. This means you are coming at this big, heavy emotional topic from very different perspectives.

Your current financial situation also influences your money mindset. However, your current situation need not dictate your future. Attitudes about money, or about anything for that matter, are not set-in stone. Remember, you can choose your thoughts and behaviors.

Assessing and perhaps reprogramming your attitude about money can open up new opportunities because what you believe about money, yourself and the world shapes how your life will unfold. Every day you have the power to make decisions that will move you forward financially or set you back.

Swiss Touch: The Global Retirement Index — a comparison for best practices in retirement policy — consistently shows that Switzerland ranks among the top three countries worldwide for retirement taking into consideration health, finances and material well-being.

Take Stock

Each culture has different ways of evaluating, discussing and using money. Your cultural identity impacts every aspect of your finances. Once you identify cultural influences around you, you can adapt your financial decisions accordingly.

A ten-year global study showed that household savings rates differ dramatically between countries. For example, Finland had the lowest rate at -0.4% of disposable income while Switzerland had the highest, 17.6 %. Reasons for savings vary, too. In the United States, most people save for unexpected expenses or retirement, while people in other countries tend to save less and rely more on generous pension funds. Types of savings also differ. Cultures, such as the US, prefer investments in home ownership over savings accounts. Understanding various cultures can enable positive financial decisions suitable to all.

What's more, attitudes toward money can differ *even* within a country! In a specific study in Switzerland, it was found that three main types of attitudes towards money co-existed: prestige and power; money management; and goal oriented. Remarkably, the attitudes differed significantly across Switzerland's linguistic regions.

Beyond culture, your beliefs will drive your behavior. This will likely not surprise you since you have already learned about beliefs in the Spiritual Dimension. Henry Ford once said, "Whether you believe you can do a thing or not, you are right." Believing in and embracing change makes the impossible possible.

What you believe about money is your point of departure for financial security.

Ramsey Solutions conducted a study of over 10,000 millionaires. One of the most fascinating findings was that 97% of millionaires *believed they could become millionaires*. It was within their control, and *they* held the key to *their* success. That mindset — not an inheritance, a fancy education or wealthy parents — is what allowed them to succeed.

Money principles are a set of external and internal factors that determine how you feel about money. They help shape the decisions you make — for better or worse. Principles are shaped through childhood experiences, culture, social groups, goals and ambitions. For example, if you value buying whatever you want, but your spending habits put you in debt, it's time to realign.

When you align your money values with your goals and actions, you can lead a more secure, more fulfilling life that you can afford.

Swiss Touch: In 2020, The Economist magazine Intelligence Unit rated Zurich as one of the three most expensive cities in the world — tying with Paris and Hong-Kong. Despite being pricey, Swiss citizens get value for money as it consistently ranks among the top 10 countries worldwide for overall *quality of life* and among the top five as *the best countries to live in.*

ELLEN'S JOURNEY

Growing up in the States in the 70's was all about excess and *big-ness*. Big cars, big food, big houses, big waste. Imagine my anxiety in 2013 when my adopted country, Switzerland, announced a tax on all garbage bags. Yes, a large 30-liter bag would now ring in at about $6! I panicked and lost sleep wondering how I would manage a household and family of five with a bag-a-day habit. Mindset — impossible!

Yet, the impossible happened. I began by discussing with my family. Our Gen Z kids were onboard with an encouraging ecological attitude. I wanted that Gen Z cool attitude and (even more) NOT TO WASTE

MONEY ON GARBAGE! Within days of the tax imposition, we organized recycling containers and embraced green savings. Within a month, our 30-liter-per-day ($35/week) habit changed to three liters-per-week. We all participated (and still do) in recycling duties with a proud obsession not to fill that pricey bag!

To take stock, ask yourself the following questions: How important to you are the things you spend most on? Do you save for something specific or for the sake of saving? What's holding you back from financial freedom? Your answers will reveal whether your current values would limit or enhance your financial future.

From Scarcity to Abundance

At this point in your life, you've experienced events which have formed your financial mindset. You now operate from that mature mental space.

If you're afraid to spend or to not have enough money, you operate from a *scarcity mindset*. Your decisions around earning and spending are likely frugal, uncertain or fearful.

This *scarcity* mindset or *negative money script* can have disastrous effects on your financial situation. If you focus on lack and *scarcity*, then that *will* be your result.

An *abundance* mindset considers every possible favorable outcome for your financial situation. It focuses on what you *do* have and limitless opportunities, rather than on what you *don't*. Abundance is not about money, it's about mentality. As Henry David Thoreau once said, "Wealth is the ability to truly experience life."

So, when it comes to finances, an *abundance* mindset allows you to break the habits you repeat out of fear and insecurity. This leads to more creativity, joy, happiness and appreciation.

An *abundance* mindset in life also means you focus on progress and positivity. For example, if you start a new business and you work with

104

the certainty that you will succeed, the fear of not making enough money is not an option. Your abundance mindset asserts that regardless of your finances, you will always make more than you need. At 50+, you have the experience and confidence to *abundantly* embark on whatever journey you want.

Money is like any energy, it needs to flow, move and be utilized in order to achieve its purpose. Using money with the right intentions, you activate its positive energy. By embodying an *abundance* mindset, your financial life will flow towards the energy you give it.

Abundance means knowing that you have everything you need in this moment, A positive script. It's not about more stuff. Abundance comes from circulating your wealth in such a way that creates more joy in the world with a balance of inflows and outflows for a secure future.

People with an abundance mindset are *creators*, not *reactors,* while those with a scarcity mindset wait for things to happen and then react. Which way would you like to imagine your future?

Mind the Gap

Acquiring knowledge is a question of choice. Numerous options exist — online, offline, cost-free or affordable — to choose from. Financial literacy is no exception. Read on to learn more, free of charge!

The Organization for Economic Cooperation and Development (OECD) defines financial literacy, as not only the knowledge and understanding of financial concepts and risks, but also the skills, motivation, and confidence to apply that knowledge to make effective decisions across a range of financial contexts, to improve the financial well-being of individuals and society, and to enable participation in economic life.

Research consistently shows that only about one-third of the global population is financially literate and that low levels of financial literacy correlate with ineffective spending and financial planning,

The Financial Industry Regulatory Authority's work shows that women score consistently lower than men on financial literacy measures.

This reveals financial vulnerabilities and lack of confidence in specific populations, including older women. This *gender-gap* impacts women's long-term financial well-being.

Both men and women *must* acknowledge that this financial literacy gender-gap exists and aim to close it. Sometimes this gap arises from life circumstances, such as couples sharing financial accounts or an imbalance in financial education relying on one person's decisions rather than teaming-up.

Due to less time in the workforce, mothers who have been absent to raise children, often earn less. Women, however, tend to live longer. As women's power and influence in the world expands, it's critical for everyone to take more responsibility in closing the gaps. Nobody can afford to remain uneducated, underinvested, or disengaged from their finances.

The current retirement landscape means older adults are more active, energetic, healthy and capable of launching new careers. Financial planning must be at the top of your mind.

With life expectancies rising, many pensions and social welfare systems are shifting the responsibility for retirement saving from governments and employers to employees. Financial markets are changing rapidly, with new and more complex products. Financial technology is revolutionizing the way we make decisions, from e-banking to online advice.

Think about it; how big is the *literacy gap* between what you *need* to know and what you *admittedly do* know about your financial future?

For all older adults, the path to closing the gaps toward financial security begins with essential money management. Ongoing skillful attention to spending and saving will relieve ungrounded fears and allow you to thrive within your means. Learning how to budget, avoid scams, apply for benefits and manage credit cards along with your willingness to embrace responsibility will help you stay secure and independent for longer.

Financial planning means upskilling and solid preparation. It can take some legwork, but knowing where you are now, and where you want to be in the future, can make the difference between merely surviving or thriving beyond retirement age. This will create financial freedom.

Green Thumb: Sustainable investing has gained momentum with investors increasingly looking to align investment decisions with modern values. Sustainable investing aims to positively impact the environment and society while providing a financial return comparable to traditional investments.

Plan Now, Play Later

Did you know that experts say you should always have three to six months' worth of living expenses in an emergency fund?

John F. Kennedy said it best, "The time to repair the roof is when the sun is shining." So, whatever your current situation, the sooner you prepare the better.

Your money needs direction and a plan to meet your life goals. The structure of this plan stems from everything you have read in this Dimension, alongside three fundamental considerations.

First, know precisely where you stand. Often neglected, it's precision that matters, like a watch. If you only have a rough idea where you stand financially, you'll roughly get what you need. By understanding your needs versus wants and how much fluctuates in and out, you will gain clarity, control, confidence and freedom.

Second, identify what you will need in the future in both worst and best-case scenarios. As you age, the way you earn and spend change. Depending on your plans and unexpected life events, you may need to save or invest differently. Travel, housing, hobbies, health and family costs are all part of your considerations.

Third, identify options. Understanding optimal ways to manage your finances and planning for the long term is where many of us need support. Retirement and insurance plans have evolved to reflect demographics, cultures, economic and currency fluctuations, to name a few.

Financial wellness is about building healthy money habits one cent at a time! Know your money mindset, stay true to your core values, track routines and spending, and leverage your skills and resources to build a life you love.

Money Talks

For many, the subject of money carries a certain stigma, especially when discussing income, retirement savings, or other personal financial details.

Although there are good intentions behind avoiding the topic, talking about money puts you at an advantage when it comes to financial wellness. Would you ever avoid talking about other important topics, such as education or health?

By having open conversations about money, you will be better informed. Financial advisors can offer professional advice, but here are some other settings where money-talk can benefit you — and likely others, too.

Among like-minded professionals or colleagues, respectful, candid discussions about usual levels of remuneration can be very useful — especially for entrepreneurs. This does not necessarily mean revealing exactly how much individuals make, but rather conversing about benchmarks and income ranges in specific contexts. Though talking about income remains somewhat of a social taboo, it's more and more accepted and even *expected* to know what you're worth. Without talking about money, how will you even know if there *is* a gap to close? Open communication can avoid frustrations or embarrassment due to under or over-compensating yourself and others.

With friends and family. Open conversations about money with close friends, family and especially your partner, give you a greater chance of fulfilling your saving and spending intentions. Accountability partners who can check in with you, keep you on track, and celebrate your progress will also prevent you from ignoring or hiding from your financial state.

Knowledge is power. Though it might be uncomfortable to talk about money, it's a subject everyone has to deal with, no matter their age or financial status. An honest flow of information and conversation will likely always benefit those involved, especially children and partners. People tend to feel a sense of relief from discussing their situation and possible fears with regard to money. This, in turn, allows them to make better decisions, avoid critical mistakes, and set attainable targets.

The more you discuss and share thoughts about finances, the more you open the doors for others to do the same and the closer to financial freedom you will be. Who would want to hide from that?

Financial Shake-Up Wrap-Up

Though the world's greatest financial worry is retirement, now is the ideal time to be money savvy.

- Every culture has different ways of valuing, discussing and using finances
- Understanding how you relate to money is critical
- Limiting beliefs around money can change how you think and decide. You must be prepared to get rid of anything holding you back
- Reviewing and taking stock of your own attitude about money can open up new opportunities
- Planning and getting ready now will save you stress and increase your chances for financial freedom
- An *abundance* mindset lets you break the habits you practice out of fear and insecurity, leading to more creativity, joy, happiness and appreciation
- Staying true to your core values and leveraging your financial skills and resources will help you build the life you deserve.

Elevate Now!

Starting now, *count* how often you think about money. Try to notice if your thoughts are positive, negative, or neutral and assess how you feel about that.

Stuff we love to count:

- Spending
- Saving
- How often we speak openly about money
- How we feel when we choose to, or not to, purchase something.

We invite you to use your cost-free *Thrive-Guide* to find resources to upskill your thoughts and projections around money.

8

ᵑmble Your Gears

ᵒossible and as slowly as necessary.”
Alain Berset

ᵑnnected and interdependent. Through wak-
-up, you have discovered *why* they matter and
ᵗ step is to go from *knowing* to *doing*, and from
rspective, *elevating you.*

ing where you want to *stay, forever.* Like a
ᵉach individual Gear turns smoothly and that
ᵈ rewound periodically. You know that quick
. Timeless solutions require deep change at

ult. In fact, the easier and smaller, the better.
ᵉ baby steps that you are confident to achieve
ᵗh-other. It's like climbing a mountain. Each
ᵘu go at your own pace and rest in between.
mit and look back at how far you've come,
ᵗ and incredibly cool — no matter your pace

As you now know, those who prepare for life after 50 tend to flourish. Those who neglect it, often regret and decline. A calibrated plan is your best resource for ageing well. So, it's time to assess and adjust precisely for what *you* want next. Now, it's about committing to make *you* a priority.

Choosing to thrive is your decision to invest energy *toward* what you desire. Choose *progress* over *perfection* and you will not fail. Committing to *do* is more effective than committing to *avoid* doing something. Just think, which thought inspires you more: 'I will enjoy a piece of quality chocolate in moderation' or 'I will avoid chocolate'? For chocolate lovers, it's not too tough to choose, is it?

Your commitments can be long-term or short-term. Long-term aspirations give you a sense of direction while short-term provide stepping-stones to keep you on track. Using both types, you have a better chance of long-lasting lifestyle change.

Big-picture intentions are defined by your values and heart. For example, 'I want to be fit' or 'I want to look forward to going to work'. They represent ongoing efforts without specifying a point in time. Big-picture focus gives you flexibility in deciding how to get where you want to be.

Short-term, specific, action-based objectives provide detail about what you will do and when you will do it. For example, 'I will register for a language course this week' or 'I will spend two hours understanding my finances each month'. If big-picture intentions provide the *why* for habit change, short-term commitments provide the *how*. Though they are less flexible, they keep you engaged thanks to quick feedback.

Once you decide which Gear you're ready to shift, put your watch into motion keeping in mind that it will naturally need rewinding or repairs along the way. By fine-tuning your life, you're simply shifting Gears, which is a sure sign of persistence and fulfillment.

As you elevate your awareness and fulfil your intentions, your confidence grows. So, reward yourself and use your enhanced self-efficacy to keep going.

This book is to get you started. The next part — your *Thrive-Guide* — will accompany you every step of the way from *knowing* to *doing* to *being*. Team-up with it and ease into calibration when and where it inspires you most.

Today *is* the beginning of whatever journey you choose.

To stay connected with like-minded people. Our Wake-Up, Shake-Up, Thrive! community is always here for you so you won't grow old waiting.

We hope you enjoy bringing to life that itch that moved you to read this book. It's time to elevate beyond your dreams. Time to make a difference — with a *cool Swiss touch!* Remember, time waits for no one...

Thrive-Guide

Welcome to your *Thrive-Guide*! Are you ready to go from *knowing* to *doing*, and then from *doing* to *being*? Your Thrive Guide is designed to *activate and elevate your* journey at *your* pace. Your own personal coach to refer to anytime, anywhere. Through years of workshops and coaching people like you, we have explored and mastered hundreds of tools and strategies to support and encourage your forward journey.

Each of the Five Dimensions — Physical, Emotional, Intellectual, Spiritual and Financial — has its own section and own specific style.

You'll discover our selection of tried and tested exercises, checklists, assessments, tips, and games designed to nudge and support your progress all the way.

We have tried our best to keep this fun. Remember, playfulness is part of preserving our youth!

One of our favorite tools is the *Wheel of Life*. Some claim it's been around for over a thousand years. We have adapted this ancient tool into the *Balloon of Life* diagrammed below. It's a visualization tool to identify the dimensions of your life arranged in a circle like the sections of a hot-air balloon ready to elevate.

Measuring your satisfaction in each Dimension is useful to identify how balanced your life feels and potential areas of imbalance.

Here's how it works:

1. Assess your satisfaction with each Dimension based on your reading
2. Place a point on your balloon, for each Dimension. Rate them from 1-5, with dissatisfaction toward the center (1) and satisfaction toward the outside (5)
3. Look at the shape of your balloon and plan your focus. You will likely choose to prioritize points near the middle because a fuller balloon will elevate better, while a deflated balloon withers and falls
4. Advance at your own pace and track your progress by adjusting your point(s) as you progress in a given Dimension
5. Your balloon will inflate and deflate as you grow and change. You can recreate your own new balloons — or wheels — to further break down any Dimension at any time.

Don't forget, reward yourself along the way and use the latest cool, confident you to continue your forward momentum. For inspiration and fun, we've included a list of potential small, medium and big reward ideas at the end of your *Thrive-Guide*.

"There are many spokes on the wheel of life. First, we are here to explore new possibilities." Ray Charles

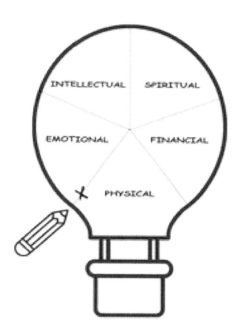

Your Wheel of Life

Physical: Your Basecamp

In the Physical Dimension, we have chosen to move you from knowing to doing through SMART goals.

SMART is an acronym that has been credited to both Peter Drucker and G.T. Doran. This goal-setting term is now used by managers, coaches and individuals in all areas of life. It stands for:

S — specific
M — measurable
A — attainable
R — realistic
T — time oriented

SMART goals can help keep you on track and remind you of your priorities, so you can follow through with every workout or healthy meal you've planned. Being accountable to what you set is the only way to maintain real long-term consistency, which is essential in the Physical Dimension. We also like to add '+' to the acronym standing for *positive*.

Which of the following SMART goals inspires you more?

I will stop eating chocolate today

versus

I will limit chocolate to 1 square per day and observe how it makes me feel.

By thinking SMART+, we reframe intentions so that they are motivating rather than discouraging.

By taking small, realistic steps and tracking your changes over time, you'll be more likely to meet or exceed your goals. Once you reach your goal, remember to recognize and reward yourself for all you've accomplished. Get a massage, indulge in a long soak in the bath or replace your old gym shoes.

You'll notice that sometimes SMART+ goals begin with the words I observe. Simply *observing* and *noticing* things sharpens awareness about your current habits and can powerfully nudge you off your old path on to a new one.

Below we propose a selection of SMART+ goals for each sub-section of the Physical Dimension. Feel free to tweak, add or subtract to meet your current state of wellness and *take your time,* moving at your own pace. Feel free to create sub-balloons if you find it useful to assess and track progress of sub-sections.

Nutrition

My Fruits and Vegetables SMART+ Goals

- ☐ I observe and ensure my fruit and veg intake is half my life: portions (Nutrition Apps can be helpful)
- ☐ I use my fist to measure one portion. So, about one apple, one banana, a fistful of carrots
- ☐ I make it Visible! Numerous studies show that we eat what we see! So, think about keeping fruits in a bowl, small veggies cleaned and handy in the front of the fridge
- ☐ I explore new, local, organic and seasonal fruits and veg whenever possible, because they contain maximum vitamins and minerals, support the local economy and protect our environment
- ☐ I leave on the skin. Maintaining the skin or peel on vegetables and fruits wherever possible helps ensure adequate fiber intake, lower blood sugar and longer satiety — all of which are more compromised with age
- ☐ I make it colorful. The more colorful the variety of fruits and veg, the greater source of multiple vitamins and minerals and no single fruit or vegetable provides all the needed nutrients
- ☐ I don't shy away from frozen or canned fruits and vegetables. Reading labels to ensure minimum additives. I keep frozen peas, beans, spinach or Asian mix, canned tomatoes, artichokes, pick-

les or beets on hand in case time is short remembering this quick option is often better than none at all!

My Fiber SMART+ Goals

- ☐ I read food labels or information to ensure I keep intake at 21 grams per day for women and 30 grams per day for men
- ☐ I eat naturally fiber-rich fruits, vegetables, maintaining the fiber-full skin wherever possible
- ☐ I replace white flour with whole grains like whole wheat, bran or oats
- ☐ I integrate legumes like lentils, chickpeas or beans replacing other carbohydrates
- ☐ I increase fiber intake gradually throughout weeks or days

My Whole Grains — Carbohydrates SMART+ Goals

- ☐ I observe adequate carbohydrate intake (Nutrition Apps can be helpful)
- ☐ I use my fist to measure one portion of carbohydrates
- ☐ I eat a variety of whole grains and healthy carbohydrates
- ☐ I observe and limit added sugars to stabilize blood-sugar, maintain weight and mood
- ☐ I move! Muscles burn glucose from carbohydrates

My Fats SMART+ Goals

- ☐ I observe adequate fat intake (Nutrition Apps can be helpful)
- ☐ I replace both saturated fats and trans-fats with unsaturated fats whenever possible
- ☐ I limit consumption of fried, industrialized and processed foods
- ☐ I observe my omega-3 and aim to consume it regularly
- ☐ I limit oil in cooking by steaming, baking and grilling
- ☐ I read food labels to understand *mg* type of fat and calories

My Water SMART+ Goals

- ☐ I observe adequate water intake (Nutrition Apps can be helpful)
- ☐ I choose water over all other beverages first, especially if exercising

☐ I drink water if I feel hungry. Thirst is often confused with hunger

☐ I keep a water bottle near me at work, in the car or kitchen as a reminder

My Alcohol SMART+ Goals

☐ I observe how my body feels and changes with alcohol consumption as I age

☐ I limit wine to one glass per day for women, two for men

☐ I choose quality over quantity

My Coffee SMART+ Goals

☐ I observe how my body reacts to coffee, caffeine and dry skin

☐ I observe how I feel and sleep when drinking coffee by testing with decaffeinated

☐ I am aware of high-calorie add-ins such as sugar or cream

My Protein SMART+ Goals

☐ I observe adequate protein intake (Nutrition Apps can be helpful)

☐ I aim to integrate one portion of proteins at all meals and snacks

☐ I vary between animal and vegetable protein such as legumes

☐ I upgrade animal protein quality considering environment and animal protection

☐ I favor fatty fish like salmon to ensure healthy ageing omega-3 fatty acids

My Mindful Eating SMART+ Goals

☐ I do a *Mindful Eating Assessment* on the website amihungry.com

☐ When I feel like eating, I *pause* to ask myself 'Am I Hungry?'

☐ When I am *not* hungry, I get curious as to what might be triggering my desire to eat

☐ I eat with a beginner's mind, using my five senses — sight, smell, touch, sound, taste — every time I eat

- ☐ I *sit down* to take at least 30 minutes to chew and truly enjoy my food — this also aids digestion which can be more difficult as I age
- ☐ If I do not enjoy my food, I do not eat it
- ☐ I *pause* during my meal or snack to check in with myself to see how I feel, curiously asking am I still hungry or is it just my habit to finish my plate?

Activity

My Aerobic — Cardio SMART+ Goals

- ☐ I begin gradually and seek guidance if I need it
- ☐ I walk! It's ideal for most, aiming for 10,000 steps per day
- ☐ I exercise nearly every day, alternating harder workouts with easier ones for recovery, remembering that recovery may take longer as I age
- ☐ I use or acquire good equipment, especially shoes
- ☐ I explore a variety of activities to find what suits me best and not get bored
- ☐ I listen to my body
- ☐ I drink water to stay hydrated and for energy
- ☐ I try new Apps or Step Counters if that motivates me
- ☐ I invite friends or partners to join

My Flexibility SMART+ Goals

- ☐ I seek guidance before beginning
- ☐ I try new Apps or Videos if that motivates me
- ☐ I am gentle, comfortable and relaxed
- ☐ I aim for 2-3 days per week, about 20 minutes
- ☐ I do multiple stretches of major muscle groups

My Resistance-Strength SMART+ Goals

- ☐ I ask for help if needed since proper technique is essential
- ☐ I try new Apps / Videos if that motivates me
- ☐ I start slowly and gradually increase weight or resistance
- ☐ I only use safe and well-maintained equipment

☐ I give muscles at least 48 hours to recover before my next session

Sleep

My Sleep SMART+ Goals

☐ I ensure my bedroom is quiet, dark, and cool, and my bed comfortable

☐ I try to naturally boost my melatonin levels by using low-watt light bulbs and turning off all screens at least one hour before bed

☐ I aim for a consistent sleep schedule

☐ I adjust my bedtime to match when I feel like going to bed, even if that's earlier than it used to be

☐ I don't stress if I can't get back to sleep — which is common with aging and try to focus on the feelings and sensations in my body instead

My Nutrition — Sleep SMART+ Goals

☐ I limit caffeine late in the day

☐ I avoid alcohol before bedtime

☐ I eat a medium-sized balanced meal containing all food groups

☐ I minimize liquid intake before sleep

My Activity — Sleep SMART+ Goals

☐ I do aerobic-cardio exercise regularly to release sleep promoting hormones in my body

☐ I avoid strenuous activity right before bed

☐ I practice relaxing exercises like yoga or stretching to calm my body

My 'See a doctor if' SMART+ Goals

If I experience any of the following on a regular basis, I check with a doctor. A sleep diary can be a useful tool to take to your doctor if necessary.

☐　Trouble falling asleep even though I feel tired
☐　Trouble getting back to sleep when awakened
☐　Don't feel refreshed after a night's sleep
☐　Feel irritable or sleepy during the day
☐　Difficulty staying awake when sitting still, watching television, or driving
☐　Difficulty concentrating during the day
☐　Rely on sleeping pills or alcohol to fall asleep

My Physical Dimension Elevation

Assess your satisfaction with each section of the Physical Dimension:

1.　Place a point on your balloon, for each section. Rate them from 1-5, with dissatisfaction toward the center (1) and satisfaction toward the outside (5)
2.　Look at the shape of your balloon and plan your focus. You will likely choose to prioritize points near the middle because a fuller balloon will elevate better, while a deflated balloon withers and falls
3.　Advance at your own pace and track your progress by adjusting your point(s) as you improve in a given sub-section
4.　Your balloon will inflate and deflate as you grow and change. You can recreate your own new balloons — or wheels — to further break down any sub-section any time.

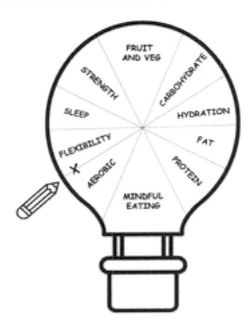

Your Physical Wheel of Life

Emotional: Your Emotional Essentials

Name It to Tame It

This daily mental workout will help you notice and name your emotions so you can take a step back and make choices about what to do with them.

1. Throughout your day and week, refer to the list of emotions below. Notice your emotion of the moment
2. Then, describe or name it — whether to yourself or out loud. For example, saying mentally 'I'm feeling angry' or 'I feel loved'. By putting your attention on words, your executive brain will take over and calm down your emotional limbic brain
3. Calmly linger over your emotion to give your executive brain time to filter and organize your reactive emotions
4. Now you have a greater capacity to choose your response in the moment
5. It's important to build your capacity to *be* with your emotions. If not, you may become fearful of them, especially negative ones, and shut them down. The cost of restricting your emotions can lead to shutting down all emotion, including positive sources of joy and pleasure.

Non-Exhaustive List of Emotions…Choose yours:

Amazed * Surprised * Astonished * Entertained * Distracted * Furious * Mad * Angry * Frustrated * Annoyed * Sad * Pensive * Discouraged * Excited * Happy * Joyful * Included * Disgusted * Fearful * Worried * Loved * Relieved * Satisfied * Lonely * Disappointed * Lost * Miserable * Anxious * Terrified * Panicked * Bitter * Insulted * Uncomfortable * Proud * Recognized * Rewarded * Amused

P.S. Some emotions may be similar, yet not exactly the same. Try to be specific. If you feel short of vocabulary and want this exercise to have more impact, many interesting inventories can be found online. Be curious!

Bias by Us

According to the World Health Organization, age bias requires a new understanding of ageing by all generations.

They propose a short online Quiz as a first step. You can check your attitudes against commonly held views of ageing and find out how much you know on the World Health Organization website (www.who.int).

Five-Minute Exercise

The following five-minute exercise will help to raise your awareness about instinctive and unconscious bias.

1. Write down the names of six to ten people you trust. Not family
2. Now, observe the names. What do you discover? How diverse is your list? How similar to you are those you trust?

Studies show that, in general, people extend not only greater trust, but also greater positive regard, cooperation, and empathy to people like themselves. This preference is largely instinctive and unconscious, yet important.

Seven-Day Exercise

This seven-day thought provoking exercise will help you become more aware of your age bias. Journaling is often an eye-opening experience.

Over seven days, record negative thoughts you regularly have or say. Train yourself to catch these negative thoughts or statements. You are training yourself to boost your self-awareness — a critical part of Emotional Intelligence.

Your list may look like this:

• I'm too old to dance
• I cannot keep up with younger people's speed anymore

- Having a *senior moment*
- You look good for your age
- You're young at heart
- Old is not beautiful
- You're too old to learn
- I'm too old to change.

Catch as many as you can — after all, nobody is looking!

Further Thinking

As you record negative thoughts on ageing and ageism, think about:

1. Where might these thoughts be coming from?
2. Are they really true?
3. How can you turn them around?

Example 1*: Having a senior moment*

1. It is commonly said by everyone often
2. No. Everybody, at all ages forgets sometimes
3. I replace *senior moment* by *senior magic,* so much more playful.

Example 2: *You look good for your age*

1. Marketing and media stress that older people aren't supposed to look good
2. Look and age are not necessarily associated. I can decide to look *good* at any age
3. I stop associating looks and with age by saying: 'You look good!'

Choose Positive

Positivity is like a muscle. It needs continuous workouts to stay limber and strong. The column on the left represents some nudges to help you choose positivity now. On the right, write down everything that comes to mind. Keep in mind that positivity is contagious, so your positive vibes will boomerang back.

Nudge	My positivity workout
I speak to myself as if I were my best friend	My positive self-talk:
I spend time with positive thinkers	My positive people:
I smile more	My daily/weekly smile target:
I appreciate my surroundings	Observation of my environment:
I celebrate	My big and small reasons to celebrate:
I read for fun	My pleasure reading:
I pay attention to the words I use to incite positivity	I replace *but* with *and* to connect two phrases in a sentence, because the word *but* essentially negates the first phrase.

Passion Power

We have assembled five questions to help you power-up your passions — whether you know them or not!

1. Imagine an ideal day. How does it start and what do you see?
2. What do you enjoy doing so much that you lose track of time?
3. What can you talk about for hours that makes you light up and feel excited?
4. What are you really good at?
5. What give you a sense of purpose?
6. Discover your passion power by intersecting your answers.

From Head to Heart

There are many useful tools to improve emotional well-being. One of them we find innovative is HeartMath. Their products, tools and techniques are based on over 25 years of scientific research conducted on the psychophysiology of stress, emotions, and the interactions between the heart and brain.

The free online HeartMath Experience video provides five practical tools to explore connecting your head to heart. You will learn to change your heart rhythm pattern to create *physiological coherence* between emotions and body. Try the free 90-minute discovery video on the HeartMath website (www.heartmath.com).

Ups and Downs

It's useful to stand back to look forward. Exploring your *life curve* can help you identify trends and triggers.

First draw a line from today back to your childhood — any age. Identify positive events that made the line go up and negative events that made it go down. At each critical up or down, name the event and its approximate month and year. Complete your life curve(s) from childhood until today.

Second, next to each up and down, write the emotions you remember feeling. Explore what happened that made you feel that way. Observe whether there is pattern in your emotional imprint. Notice what you did to bounce back from negative events and how long it took. For positive emotions, consider what you did with your positive energy.

Understanding the impact that events have on us and how we react to them is important to understanding how to face obstacles and to seek out positive emotional energy for the future. Creating, visualizing and feeling your life curve is an experience revealing that it's not so much what happens that matters but what you make of it. Sharing your in-sights out loud with someone you trust is even more impactful.

Emotions at Work

We all have to deal with negative emotions at work sometimes and learning how to cope with these feelings is important because negative behaviors at work can seriously harm your professional reputation and productivity. We will focus on coping with *negative* emotions in the workplace. As long as *positive* emotions are shared constructively and professionally, they're great to have at work and don't need specific coping strategies!

Here we overview the most common negative emotions experienced in the workplace and how you can strategize around them productively.

Begin by recognizing what causes your negative emotions and which types of feelings you face most often. Then, when those emotions begin to appear, you can learn to interrupt the cycle with your strategy.

Frustration at Work

Frustration usually occurs when you feel stuck, trapped, or unable to move forward in some way. It could be caused by a colleague blocking your favorite project, a disorganized boss or being put on hold. Whatever the reason, it's important to deal with feelings of frustration quickly, because they can easily lead to more negative emotions, such as anger.

Suggestions for dealing with frustration:

- Stop and evaluate, look at the situation and ask yourself why you feel frustrated. Record it. Be specific.
- Find something positive about the situation to look at things differently. This small mindset shift can improve your mood. Remember your *Sage*?
- Give feedback to the source of frustration whenever possible. Take three deep breaths and share with the person who created the tension precisely how you feel and the impact it had.

Worry at Work

With all the fear and anxiety that comes with job insecurity, it's no wonder that many people worry about their jobs. This can easily get out of control and can impact your mental health, your productivity, and your readiness to take actions at work.

Suggestions for dealing with worry:

- Take three deep breaths to allow your brain the oxygen it needs to think clearly
- Validate with yourself if the cause of your worry or fear is a fact or a probability

- Avoid surrounding yourself with people who are worried, stressed or anxious
- Focus on what you can do to broaden your thinking
- Journal your worries to evacuate them.

Anger at Work

Out-of-control anger is perhaps the most destructive emotion that people experience in the workplace. It's also the emotion that most of us don't handle very well.

Suggestions for dealing with anger:

- Watch for early signs of anger and learn to recognize them when they begin. Remember, you can *choose* how you react
- If you start to get angry, stop what you're doing, close your eyes, and practice deep-breathing. Breathing reduces your heart rhythm, interrupts your angry thoughts, and it helps put you back on a more positive path
- Picture yourself when you're angry. Imagine how you look and behave when you're angry, it gives you a different perspective on the situation
- Give feedback to the source of frustration whenever possible. Communicate with the person who created the tension and explain exactly how you feel and the impact it had.

Dislike at Work

We've probably all had to work with someone we don't like, but it's important to be professional, no matter what. Remember, we don't dislike someone for who they are, but for how they behave.

Suggestions for working with people you dislike:

- Be respectful and treat the person with courtesy as you would treat anyone else
- Pause what you're doing, close your eyes and take three deep breaths. Interrupting your emotions allows you to use your non-judgmental discernment to think about why that person behaves in such a way

133

- Be proactive and set the example. If the other person is rude or unprofessional, firmly explain that you refuse to be treated that way and calmly leave the room, even virtual.

Disappointment/Unhappiness at Work

Dealing with disappointment or unhappiness at work can be difficult and most likely will impact your productivity. If you've just suffered a major disappointment, your energy will probably be low, you might be afraid to take risks which may hold you back from achievements at work.

Here are some proactive steps to cope with disappointment and unhappiness:

- Record your thoughts. Once you identify the problem, start brainstorming ways to solve it or work around it. A trusted other can help broaden your perspective. Remember, you always have the power to change your emotions
- Adjust your intentions
- If you are truly unhappy at work, maybe it's time to change
- Smile! Forcing a smile, or even a grimace, onto your face can often make you feel happy. Try it, you may be surprised!

Intellectual: Gearing Yourself Up

Your Real Brain Teaser

Living a brain-healthy lifestyle works! By taking certain actions it's proven you can keep your brain healthy.

Here are our Top-10 actions to sharpen — and keep sharp — your mental skills.

1. **Test your recall**

Make a list — grocery items, things to do, or anything else that comes to mind — and memorize it. An hour or so later, see how many items you can recall. Make the list as challenging as possible for the greatest mental stimulation.

2. **Let the music play**

Learn to play a musical instrument or join a choir. Studies show that learning something new and complex over a longer period of time is ideal for the ageing mind.

3. **Do math in your head**

Figure out problems without the aid of a pencil, paper, or computer. You can make this more difficult — and athletic — by walking at the same time.

4. **Take a cooking class**

Cooking uses a number of senses — smell, touch, sight, and taste — which involve different parts of the brain.

5. **Learn a foreign language**

The listening and hearing stimulate the brain. What's more, a rich vocabulary has been linked to a reduced risk for cognitive decline.

6. **Create word pictures**

Visualize the spelling of a word in your head, and then try to think of other words that begin (or end) with the same two letters.

7. **Draw a map from memory**

After returning home from visiting a new place, try to draw a map of the area. Repeat this exercise each time you go somewhere new.

8. **Challenge your taste buds**

When eating, try to identify individual ingredients in your meal, including subtle herbs and spices.

9. **Refine your hand-eye coordination**

Take up a new hobby that involves fine motor skills, such as knitting, drawing, painting, or assembling a puzzle.

10. **Learn a new sport.**

Start doing an athletic exercise that requires both mind and body, such as yoga, golf, or tennis.

Fire to Wire

The daily practice of visualizing your dreams as already complete can rapidly accelerate your achievement of those dreams, goals, and ambitions.

All you have to do is set aside a few minutes a day. The best times are when you're most relaxed. Maybe when you first wake up, after meditation or prayer, or right before you go to bed.

Try these three steps:

One: Imagine sitting in a movie theater, the lights dim, and then the movie starts. It's a movie of you doing perfectly whatever it is that you want to do better. See as much detail as you can create, including your clothing, the expression on your face, small body movements, the environment and any other people that might be around. Add in any sounds you would be hearing — traffic, music, other people talking, cheering. And finally, recreate in your body any feelings you think you would be experiencing as you engage in this activity.

Two: Get out of your chair, walk up to the screen, open a door in the screen and enter into the movie. Now experience the whole thing again from inside of yourself, looking out through your eyes. This is called an embodied image rather than a distant image. It will deepen the impact of the experience. Again, see everything in vivid detail, hear the sounds you would hear, and feel the feelings you would feel.

Three: Walk back out of the screen that is still showing the picture of you performing perfectly, return to your seat in the theater, reach out and grab the screen and shrink it down to the size of a biscuit. Then, bring this miniature screen up to your mouth, chew it up and swallow it. Imagine that each tiny piece — just like a hologram — contains the full picture of you performing well. Imagine all these little screens traveling down into your stomach and out through the bloodstream into every cell of your body. Then imagine that every cell of your body is lit up with a movie of you performing perfectly. It's like one of those appliance store windows where all the televisions are tuned to the same channel.

When you have finished this process — it should take less than five minutes — you can open your eyes and go about your business. If you make this part of your daily routine, you will be amazed at how much improvement you will see in your life.

Time to Play!

Research shows that regularly solving crossword puzzles can improve your life in a variety of ways:

- Improve brain function
- Lower dementia risks
- Cultivate vocabulary
- Improve verbal skills
- Increase your knowledge base
- Relieve stress
- Feel calmer and happier
- Boost your mood
- Strengthen relationships.

To get you started, head to our website www.wakeupshakeupthrive.com to find a crossword puzzle based on this book!

Our Top 10 Ways to Have More Fun:

1. Set the goal of playing more. After all, what's the point of setting a goal like being thin, having more money or having your own business if you're not enjoying yourself?
2. **Decide what fun means for you by making** a list of things that you enjoyed doing as a kid. Go over your list and highlight what still sounds appealing. Then explore what you want to try!
3. Schedule time to play in your agenda, because if you don't schedule it, it's unlikely to happen.
4. **Create a play drawer for** those times when you need a break from life or work, and you just want to be silly. You might include puzzles, board games, coloring books, Lego's — whatever inspires you!
5. **Combine fun with other activities.** Think of the things on your to-do list and then look for ways to combine them to make them more fun.
6. **Have more fun at work.** Brainstorm with colleagues how you can bring more fun and humor into the workplace.
7. **Make playdates with your significant other to** strengthen your relationship and keep playfulness alive.
8. **Befriend a fun person because the** people you relate with will have an enormous impact on your life.
9. **Hang out with kids who** innately know how to play and have fun.
10. Add creativity to daily activities such as singing while you cook or dancing while brushing your teeth.

Stage Your Change

The internet offers many online tests to see how flexible you are and how you adapt to change. These can be interesting, however accompanied with some self-reflection:

Think about a major life change you have experienced.

* Do you recognize your stages of change?
* How did you manage them?
* Where did you succeed and where did you get stuck?

Use this learning to determine how well you're Geared-up for the path before you. Remember, embracing flexibility creates positive change.

A Word on Books

If you've gotten out of the habit of reading books, here are some tips to turn that page!

* Integrate reading time into your regular routine
* Double task by reading a book while you're doing something else that doesn't require your full attention (like indoor cycling)
* Join a book club (or create one!) to hold yourself accountable
* Read outside your comfort zone to discover new experiences
* Read while traveling
* Replace screen-time (or another bad habit) with a good book
* Get good recommendations.

Digital Divide

In this age of technology, digital literacy is invaluable in life.

Consider your responses to the following questions:

* Can you work effectively and safely, online?
* Can you search for information and find the appropriate information quickly?

- Do you know how to tell if the information you find is relevant and from a good source?
- Do you know how to make the best of online networking tools like Facebook, LinkedIn and Twitter?
- Do you know how to present yourself online and manage your *digital identity?*

How confident were you in your responses? Use your level of confidence as your baseline.

There are many cool, free, interactive and user-friendly self-assessments to see how digitally literate you are in essential computer skills and essential software skills. Each can be assessed separately, so, google away.

The Connection Game

There are different perspectives and angles you can take to ensure valuable connections beyond age 50. We have divided the connection game into three categories: meaningful, work-related and networking. Have fun playing!

1. The impact of social engagement depends upon the *meaningfulness* of interactions and on how positively you feel about them. Therefore, the benefits depend on what you do and with whom you interact.

Here are some tips to promote *meaningful* social engagement:
- ☐ Focus on the relationships and social activities you enjoy the most
- ☐ Use the internet to track down old friends with whom you've had meaningful relationships in the past
- ☐ Maintain your relationship with your partner and family because these relationships tend to become increasingly important with age
- ☐ Offer to help others, whether informally or through organizations or volunteer opportunities
- ☐ If you're shy or have trouble engaging socially, take small steps to connect with others. Practice random acts of kindness such

as sharing a smile, showing interest by asking how others are or holding a door for someone

2. Many people do much of their socializing on the job, so if you stop working it's especially important to find ways to maintain or form new social connections.

Here's how:

- [ ] Be proactive about transferring your professional or extra-professional experience through teaching, speaking, coaching or mentoring
- [ ] Expand your social network outside work, so you're more likely to cultivate various types of relationships
- [ ] Research and sign-up for a professional-interest association, community or forum to stay updated with your profession or another one that inspires you
- [ ] Volunteer or work part-time to redefine your sense of purpose

3. Networking is not a one-way-street with a limited timeline and a goal in mind. Networking is as much about *giving* as receiving. Interacting with others to exchange information, develop social or professional contacts, create and nurture relationships has never been so critical.

Here are some networking tips to consider:

- [ ] Maintain social connections with people of different ages by keeping in touch with children, millennials, schools or community
- [ ] Seek opportunities to share your knowledge, experiences, skills and tips
- [ ] Challenge yourself to try organized clubs, classes, online communities, political organizations, religious gatherings, or alumni associations
- [ ] Join a group or club such as a sports group, book club, cooking group or religious service or, start your own!
- [ ] If moving to a new house means leaving family and friends, embrace the challenge of finding new connections in your new place

Spiritual: Your Non-Material Essentials

Believe in Values

There are many ways to identify your values in order to realign. We often use the resources provided by the Barrett Values Center website. However-er, you may choose from any inventory, such as our selection below.

Select ten of the following values that most reflect what is important to you.

responsibility	achievement	adaptability
ambition	balance (home/work)	being liked
winning	caring	caution
clarity	commitment	courage
community	compassion	competence
excellence	creativity	dialogue
environment	efficiency	being positive
financial stability	ethics	forgiveness
friendship	fairness	family
humor/ fun	generosity	health
modesty	integrity	autonomy
patience	making a difference	job security
power	personal growth	reputation
respect	professional growth	recognition
risk-taking	safety	reward
wealth	trust	well-being

Take a minute to notice how these might have changed throughout your lifetime.

How do your chosen values align with your Passions?

Project into your *future*. Which of those values would you like to *live more fully* in the future? How can you make that happen?

List three small steps that will help you live your values more fully:

1.

2.

3.

Drivers and Drainers Exercise. Ask your Heart.

Your personal energy gets depleted and refilled daily. It can be improved — driven, or damaged — drained. Measuring these positive and negative impacts can give you an idea of the state of your energy and where your passions lie.

First: Take two to three minutes to spontaneously list your life *Drivers* — anything or anyone that gives you *positive energy.*

Second: Take two to three minutes to spontaneously list your *Drainers* — anything or anyone that *depletes your energy.*

Now tally it up your two lists and answer these four questions.

1. Are there more drivers or drainers present in your life?
2. Which drainers would you like less of and how can you plan that?
3. Which drivers would you like more of in your life and how can you achieve that?
4. How do your drivers and drainers compare to and align with the values you discovered in the values exercise?

Gratitude Attitude

Keep a Gratitude Journal.

Research has shown that the power of keeping a gratitude journal is extraordinary. People are 25% happier and more energetic if they keep gratitude journals, have 20% less envy and resentment, sleep 10% longer each night, wake-up 15% more refreshed, exercise 33% more and show a 10% drop in blood pressure! That definitely sounds like a cool way to age.

There's no right or wrong way to keep a gratitude journal, just be expressive about your thoughts, feelings, experiences, memories, hopes and dreams. Don't just do this exercise in your head but use the tool — phone APP, paper journal, etc. — with which you feel most comfortable.

Here Are Our Top-10 Tips to Get You Started.

1. Make *you* a priority by taking time to journal and giving yourself permission to pause, write, reflect and replenish from within
2. Plan to enjoy journaling by creating a special time and place you will look forward to
3. Include a maximum of three things you are grateful for
4. Be as specific as possible to relive the experience
5. Use any form of self-expression including drawing, colors, collaging — whatever!
6. Think of gratitude as your personal experience measured by how you *feel* no matter its size, material worth or significance
7. See all things as gifts not to be taken for granted
8. Savor surprises
9. Look for unexpected pleasures that show up differently as you evolve
10. Journal regularly — at your convenience — it's a de-stressor.

Here are three more ways to cultivate gratitude on a regular basis.

Ten-minute Gratitude Reflection

- Who has been or is the most important person in your life and why?
- What are you most afraid of?
- Who do you admire most?
- What is your most important question about life?
- What do you enjoy most about your loved ones?

Ten-minute Gratitude Exercise

- Choose two people to send an email, text, note or call
- Express your sincere gratitude
- Be specific and include how they added value to your life.

The Three Gifts Technique Developed by Shirzad Chamine

In every crisis, there are many gifts and opportunities that can be created. Confronting crisis or obstacles with these *Three Gifts* in mind can help shift your perspective in practice:

1. Gift of Knowledge. What will I learn from this crisis or obstacle that will serve me in the future? Like: *Making it through a financial crisis forced me to strive to save money for the future — just in case.*
2. Gift of Power. To what extent am I strengthening my resilience by coping with this crisis or obstacle? Like: *If it weren't for last year's broken leg, I never would have learned Spanish which allowed me to land my new job.*
3. Gift of Inspiration. Which opportunities present themselves thanks to the fact that my original plan did not happen? Like: *If it weren't for the Corona virus and everything going online, I never could have convinced my clients to work virtually.*

Latest Posture on Yoga

It may surprise you to learn that hundreds of variations of yoga exist around the world. Yoga practices can be vigorous, slow and methodical, philosophical or spiritual. They can also be playful and friendly, or more serious.

When you test various types of yoga and instructors, pay attention to your emotional and mental shifts. Notice who and what inspired you, or whether you've checked out and lost interest. The best indicator of a good fit is that you'll want to do it again.

As a starting point, below are some common yoga practices you will find online, in studios or at the gym:

Hatha is a simple practice where poses are held for several seconds or minutes. It is relatively slow and simple and good for beginners.

Yin is great for both mental and physical recovery incorporating seated, supine and prone poses often held for 5 or more minutes.

Vinyasa is a strong physical practice emphasizing flexibility, focus and discipline. Vinyasa includes many balancing and standing postures.

Bikram is intense, skillful and often sweaty. It is practiced in a hot room with many poses over hours. You should talk to your doctor prior to doing Bikram.

Alternative forms of yoga are a break away from traditional yoga's that challenge regular routines and mix in fun.

To find your best fit, consider *why* you want to practice, be honest about your personal needs and shop around to find what suits best. Here are some selection criteria to ponder as you choose:

• Your level
• How much you want to sweat
• Your workout personality
• What you want to get out of your yoga
• The sort of speed you enjoy
• Where you like practicing
• How yoga would fit into your workout routine.

Think About Mindfulness and Meditation

Although there is no right or wrong way to meditate, not all meditation styles are right for everyone. These practices require different skills and mindsets. The practice that is right for you is what feels comfortable and that you feel inspired to practice regularly. Here are nine popular types of meditation to try alone, in groups, guided or unguided:

1. Mindfulness Meditation

   Good for people who don't have a teacher to guide them. Easily practiced alone. Combines concentration with awareness. Originates from Buddhist teachings. The most popular meditation technique in the West. In mindfulness meditation you pay attention to your thoughts as they pass through your mind. You don't judge the thoughts or become involved with them. You simply observe and take note of any patterns.

2. Spiritual Meditation

   Beneficial for those who thrive in silence and seek spiritual growth. Used in Eastern religions, such as Hinduism and Daoism, and in Christian faith. Similar to prayer in that you reflect on the silence around you and seek a deeper connection with your God or Universe.

3. Focused Meditation

   Ideal for anyone who requires additional focus in their life. It involves concentration using any of the five senses. If your mind does wander, it's important to come back to the practice and re-focus.

4. Movement Meditation

   Good for people who find peace in action and prefer to let their minds wander. An active form of meditation where the movement guides you. Although most people think of yoga when they hear movement meditation, this practice may include walking through the woods, gardening qi-gong, and other gentle forms of motion.

5. Mantra Meditation

   Good for people who don't like silence and enjoy repetition. Some enjoy mantra meditation because they find it easier to focus on a word than on their breath. This type of meditation uses a repetitive sound to clear the mind. It can be a word, phrase, or sound, such as the popular 'Om'.

6. Transcendental Meditation

For those who like structure and are serious about maintaining a meditation practice. It is more customizable than mantra meditation, using a mantra or series of words that are specific to each practitioner.

7. Progressive Relaxation

Often used to relieve stress and unwind before bedtime. Also known as body scan meditation, progressive relaxation is a practice aimed at reducing tension in the body and promoting relaxation. Often, this form of meditation involves slowly tightening and relaxing one muscle group at a time throughout the body.

8. Loving-Kindness Meditation

Intended to promote compassion and kindness, ideal for those holding feelings of anger or resentment. Loving-kindness meditation is used to strengthen feelings of compassion, kindness, and acceptance toward oneself and others.

9. Visualization Meditation

Can boost mood, reduce stress levels, and promote inner peace. Visualization meditation focuses on enhancing feelings of relaxation, peace, and calmness by visualizing positive scenes or images.

Remember, ultimately it doesn't matter which meditation technique you choose. What does matter, however, is that you choose a style that allows you to integrate the qualities you experience during meditation practice — calm, empathy, mindfulness — into the rest of your day. It's best to start in small moments of time, even five or ten minutes, and grow from there.

There are plenty of free Apps, videos and tutorials online. We encourage you to try lots and choose your style!

Look Forward to Leave Behind

Leaving a positive impact on the world and others is more memorable than money, property and other tangible objects. The following exercises are destined to help you discover the things you can do now to help shape the legacy you want to leave. The following exercise has been inspired by and adapted from the article *L is for leaving a positive legacy* by The Positive Encourager Global.

Focusing on the following three things can help you create a positive legacy:

1. Relationships
2. Contributions
3. Memories.

Relationships

How can you continue to build positive relationships? Looking at your own life, how do you want to be remembered as a parent, partner, friend or colleague?

1. Describe the specific things you want to do to build positive relationships.
2. Describe the actual words you would like to hear people say about the way you related to them.

Contributions

There are many approaches to your contributions to build a better world. Some examples are:

- Aim to do positive things each day to influence a better world
- Build on your strengths
- Do satisfying work
- Use your talents — teaching, coaching, creating, etc.
- Do things that help people or the planet
- Follow your vocation, calling and passion.

1. Describe the specific things you want to do to make positive contributions to people or the planet.
2. Describe the actual words you would like to hear people say about the positive contributions you made.

Memories

You want to enjoy life, pursue experiences and have no regrets. Looking back in later years, you want to feel you have appreciated and made the most of life.

1. Describe the specific things you want to do to enjoy life and create positive memories for yourself and for others.
2. Describe the actual words you would like to say about the positive memories you created for yourself and others during your time on the planet.

Financial: Your Material Essentials

It's All Relative

Reviewing your relationship with money can lead to novel ways of thinking and open up new opportunities. However, you need to be prepared to say goodbye to beliefs that may hold you back. Once you are clear in your mind, then, and only then, can you start to change your behavior. The following key questions will raise awareness about your beliefs. We highly suggest writing down your thoughts as you go to ensure clarity, creativity and retention.

- What are the first three statements that come to mind when I think of money?
- What do these statements say about my relationship with money?
- Where do I think these statements come from?
- Are these statements serving or un-serving me?
- Which of these statements am I happy with as they are?
- What new statements about money would I be ready to commit to?

Now that you have a better feeling of your beliefs, it's worth going one step beyond in determining your relationship with money. Are you careful or fearful about how you spend? Do you spend money spontaneously or recklessly? Or do you have a relationship where you sometimes splurge, sometimes spend, but feel generally ok about your spending? Many thought-provoking resources exist online to quiz your relationship with money. We like the *How Do You Relate to Money?* quiz from Relate.org.uk.

Once you understand your relationship with money, you can more easily identify *tangible commitments about what you can do* daily, weekly, monthly or yearly to reach your goals.

Take Stock

Identify what stories around money have been in your life until now, what holds true for you, and what influence it has had on your happiness level so far.

1. To uncover your money story, start by thinking about the emotions you tie to your finances. You might feel anxious, stressed, ashamed of, worried, overwhelmed, uninterested, etc.

   Completing spontaneously the following sentences may help you start discovering unconscious emotions:

   I think money...

   People with money are...

   Money makes people...

   I would have more money if...

   In my family, money...

   If I could afford it, I would...

   I'm afraid that if I had more money, I would...

   In order to have more money, I would need to...

   When I have money, I usually...

2. What are the unhelpful money stories I want to let go of?

3. What story about money do I wish to come true in my life?

4. What steps can I take to surround myself with people who help me reach my goals?

5. What is my NEW money story?

From Scarcity to Abundance

Science on the scarcity mindset shows that small shifts in outlook can have a big impact on how well we think through problems and spot opportunities.

Recognize the Power of Your Thoughts. By taking time to notice what type of thoughts are circulating in your head, you can begin to make a conscious effort to shift your thoughts towards abundance. Here are some ideas inspired by Deepak Chopra article *10 steps to develop an abundance mindset:*

1. Focus on what you do have and not what you don't
2. Keep on the look-out for 'new' things, like what's going right for you, including opportunities, resources or relationships
3. Surround yourself with people that have an abundance mindset — who generally seem positive and see the glass as half-full instead of half-empty
4. Shift your scarcity mindset which believes that if one person wins, another loses to look for the win-win in every situation
5. Contribute. Studies show that giving makes us happier, improves health, promotes co-operation and social connection, makes us grateful for what we have and is contagious
6. Practice self-compassion to loosen your desire for perfection or having things a certain way.

Mind the Gap

Becoming financially literate happens through education, practical experience, and life lessons. Tackle one topic at a time beginning with the one you are most interested in and begin to build a solid foundation.

Regardless of where you are on your financial journey, you can always learn more to improve your future. Take some time to think about what you can do to increase your knowledge, not only for yourself, but for the next generation.

Make it your goal to find easy ways to learn about money:

- Test yourself by discovering the many online financial literacy assessments (universities, governments, private financial institutions)
- Subscribe to financial newsletters
- Listen to financial podcasts
- Read finance books
- Use specific social media
- Start to keep a budget
- Join an investment club
- Take a financial literacy class
- Share what you learn among family and friends.

Plan Now, Play Later

The landscape of the years beyond 50 has changed. *Gone* are the days of one-size-fits-all financial planning and *here* are the days of active, energetic older adults like you. Whatever your background or interests, a little financial planning can go a long way. Here are six areas to focus on for well-rounded financial planning.

1. Estate: Wills, Power of Attorney, Beneficiaries
2. Insurance: Health, Disability, Life
3. Investments: Short, Medium, Long-term goals and Retirement
4. Tax planning: Up-to-date, Tax optimization
5. Cash Management: Income, Debt, Mortgage
6. Loved Ones: Dependents (children, etc.), Living Expenses (education, etc.), Parental Care.

Money Talks

Talking openly about money can help you increase your accountability, share responsibility and transparency in your relationships as well as help you plan your financial future.
Before

- Prepare yourself with a few talking points
- When — there's never going to be a perfect time but book it!
- Where — it's best to find an area where you won't be disturbed

- Who — it very much depends on the situation, but everyone who has a stake in the discussion should be included
- Practice the conversation — visualize different scenarios, working out potential responses to what the other(s) might say.

During

- Choose to be the one to break the silence and start the conversation
- Be mindful of your emotions, as well as the emotions of the person you are talking to
- Try not to interrupt
- Avoid judgements or accusations
- Keep to the topic of finances
- Try and stay about the same eye level.

After

- Acknowledge that the conversation happened and highlight outcomes — especially positive ones
- Record and share outcomes and next steps
- Thank the other person(s).

Rewards

Brain science tells us that rewarding yourself is a crucial element of sustainable behavior change. Once you've fulfilled your intentions, use this list of small, medium and big rewards for inspiration…to gift yourself. Here are our Top-10 small, medium and big rewards ideas. You can also create your own:

Small Rewards

1. Time with your favorite person
2. A new book — purchased or borrowed — and time to read it!
3. A movie or favorite show — theater or at home
4. Your favorite food or drink
5. A home beauty treatment, like a face mask, hair-conditioning treatment, or body scrub
6. A walk outside — alone or with a close one
7. A nap
8. An afternoon indulging in your favorite craft or hobby
9. A journal full of creative exercises about positivity
10. Time to listen to beautiful music and maybe create a new playlist.

Medium-Sized Rewards

1. More time with your favorite person/people
2. A day off to do whatever you want
3. Dinner or lunch out
4. A massage, manicure or pedicure — for cool guys too!

5. Something new for your home or office: a framed print, a colorful vase or a bit of cool decor
6. A new outfit. If you're rewarding yourself for sticking to your health goals, this could be work-out Gear, pajamas or an apron
7. A cool water bottle — great for fitness and health goals
8. An amazing new perfume or cologne
9. A new laptop bag or purse
10. A sports outing like a football game or hockey match.

Big Rewards

1. Much more time with your favorite person/people
2. A high-tech item you've been wanting for a while
3. A concert, performance, or high-ticket sporting event
4. A clean house from a housekeeping service
5. A night or two at a hotel or B&B
6. A party. This could be big, but it could also be small — just a few friends to celebrate an accomplishment!
7. A hot air balloon ride — elevate!
8. A meaningful piece of jewelry
9. A professional photo shoot to give you great pictures of your amazing self
10. A dream vacation.

Acknowledgements

"Forget love — I'd rather fall in chocolate!"
Linda Marion

We began this book by sharing that the Swiss eat more chocolate than everyone else. We love chocolate. Chocolate is traditionally offered as a gift when one is an invited guest. Our way of saying *Thank You, Merci, Grazie*. We wish to acknowledge everyone who made this book possible — with chocolate.

To Paul, our dear editor, tirelessly guiding us to navigate our book writing. *We thank you with bittersweet chocolate*, the chocolate with the boldest and most intense chocolate flavor. Our working sessions were always intense and left an aftertaste allowing us to fine-tune, boil-down and whittle our book to its essentials.

To Anne, our proofreader who brought fresh air to our book through words and enhancements, elevating it like a benevolent chocolate mousse.

To Hanae, our support team, graphic artist and youthful inspiration. We thank you with *white chocolate* — the youngest of chocolates — due to its sweet, creamy texture. Your flexibility, creativity, spontaneity and ever-positive attitude kept us young through our sweet journey.

To our clients and those behind the client journeys in this book. We thank you with *chocolate with hazelnuts*. Aficionados describe hazelnuts as indulgent, distinctive, decadent, exotic with long-lasting character. This is a wonderful way to sum-up our many precious clients who have shared their stories and lives to make us who we are today and to make this book possible.

To our 50+ friends, *we thank you with dark chocolate*, which is known for its many health benefits and always, always appreciated. Our supporting friends who listened and shared our questions and thoughts for the many years of walks and talks leading up to this book. Know you too are loved, timeless and ageless…

To our families, Zied, Etienne, Adrienne, Julien & Joël, we thank you with milk chocolate. The sweetest and milkiest of all chocolates. It's a classic that we all know and love from childhood and widely regarded as the most popular type of chocolate. Without your patience, love, and encouragement, the work we do and expressing it in these words never could have come to life.

To Mom, only Hershey's chocolate will do to properly thank you for the 84+ years you devoted to loving me unconditionally, trusting me and encouraging me to live my life fully, even if it meant spending 30+ years very far from home…

To Maman, for the warmth and the generosity you share around a chocolate fondue. Thanks to you I learnt that sharing quality time with friends, families and loved ones are unique moments to cherish dearly. Your charisma, elegance and positivity has been an inspiration for many, me included.

Finally, some *dark chocolate with whole almonds* — our favorite — bold, crunchy and absolutely delicious anytime, anywhere. Thank you to *us* — to you, Dom, from me, Ellie; to you, Ellie, from me, Dom — because *we've* inspired *each other* from the day we met to *not grow old waiting*. May our cherished friendship last forever.

References

General

14 Surprising facts about growing older no one ever told you. (n.d.). Retrieved February 21, 2021, from https://www.webmd.com/healthy-aging/ss/slideshow-aging-surprises

Bloomberg.com. (n.d.). Retrieved February 21, 2021, from https://www.bloomberg.com/news/articles/2019-06-13/world-s-retirees-risk-running-out-of-money-a-decade-before-death

Bumgardner, W. (2019, December 06). How many average daily steps do people walk? Retrieved February 21, 2021, from https://www.verywellfit.com/whats-typical-for-average-daily-steps-3435736#:

Cherry, K. (2019, December 07). What are fluid intelligence and crystallized intelligence? Retrieved February 21, 2021, from https://www.verywellmind.com/fluid-intelligence-vs-crystallized-intelligence-2795004

Coxwell, K., Chen, S., & Kenton, W. (2020, February 20). 10 super surprising facts about financial success later in life. Retrieved February 21, 2021, from https://www.newretirement.com/retirement/success-later-in-life/

Emling, S. (2017, December 07). 9 facts about aging that will actually get you excited about growing older. Retrieved February 21, 2021, from https://www.huffpost.com/entry/good-things-about-aging_n_5372835

Facts about ageing. (2015, October 03). Retrieved February 21, 2021, from https://www.who.int/ageing/about/facts/en/

Heilprin, J. (2017, October 18). The numbers that show Switzerland Loves walking. Retrieved February 21, 2021, from https://www.swissinfo.ch/eng/take-a-hike_the-numbers-that-show-switzerland-loves-walking/43218498

Ikeda, d. (2018). *Unlocking the mysteries of birth & death: ... And everything in between, a buddhist view life*. Readhowyouwant com.

Khalfani-Cox, L. (n.d.). 5 SMART financial moves to make by age 50 - personal finance - SMART M... Retrieved February 21, 2021, from https://www.aarp.org/money/investing/info-04-2012/5-SMART-financial-moves.html

Rapsas, T. (2017, October 19). Five ways to stay Spiritually vibrant after age 50. Retrieved February 21, 2021, from https://www.patheos.com/blogs/wakeup-call/2017/10/five-ways-to-stay-spiritually-vibrant-after-age-50/

Schaffhauser05/23/18, D. (n.d.). Skills deficit will Imperil U.S. economy by 2030. Retrieved February 21, 2021, from https://thejournal.com/articles/2018/05/23/skills-deficit-will-imperil-u.s.-economy-by-2030.aspx

State Secretariat for Economic Affairs SECO. (n.d.). Work and rest period. Retrieved February 21, 2021, from https://www.seco.admin.ch/seco/en/home/Arbeit/Arbeitsbedingungen/Arbeitnehmerschutz/Arbeits-und-Ruhezeiten.html

Thatcher, M. (2019, October 04). 43 venerable human Aging Facts. Retrieved February 21, 2021, from https://www.factretriever.com/aging-facts

United States., Congress., Senate. (n.d.). *America's aging workforce: Opportunities and challenges: A report of the Special Committee on Aging, United States Senate.*

Vacation, public holidays, working hours. (n.d.). Retrieved February 21, 2021, from https://www.eda.admin.ch/missions/mission-onu-geneve/en/home/manual-regime-privileges-and-immunities/introduction/manual-labour-law/vacation-holidays-hours.html

Van der Elst, K. V. (n.d.). *Why we need to rethink ageing.* World Economic Forum. https://www.weforum.org/agenda/2015/01/why-we-need-to-rethink-ageing/.

World Health Organization. (n.d.). *Global Recommendations on Physical Activity for Health.*

World Health Organization. https://www.who.int/.

Physical

10 facts on ageing and health. (n.d.). Retrieved February 21, 2021, from https://www.who.int/news-room/fact-sheets/detail/10-facts-on-ageing-and-health

2015-2020 dietary guidelines. (n.d.). Retrieved February 21, 2021, from https://health.gov/our-work/food-nutrition/previous-dietary-guidelines/2015

54 shocking sleep statistics, data and trends revealed for 2021. (2021, January 21). Retrieved February 21, 2021, from https://www.sleepadvisor.org/sleep-statistics/#top_ankor

Bottle water is wasteful. (n.d.). Retrieved February 21, 2021, from https://thewaterproject.org/bottled-water/bottled_water_wasteful

Cetin, D. C., & Nasr, G. (n.d.). *Obesity in the elderly: more complicated than you think.* Cleveland Clinic journal of medicine. https://pubmed.ncbi.nlm.nih.gov/24391107/.

Charles, D. (2014, July 11). Are organic vegetables more nutritious after all? Retrieved February 21, 2021, from https://www.npr.org/sections/the-salt/2014/07/11/330760923/are-organic-vegetables-more-nutritious-after-all?t=1589033537433

Chattu, V., Manzar, M., Kumary, S., Burman, D., Spence, D., & Pandi-Perumal, S. (2018, December 20). The global problem of insufficient sleep and its serious public health implications. Retrieved February 21, 2021, from https://www.ncbi.nlm.nih.gov/pmc/articles/PMC6473877/

Choose your carbs wisely. (2020, April 17). Retrieved February 21, 2021, from https://www.mayoclinic.org/healthy-lifestyle/nutrition-and-healthy-eating/in-depth/carbohydrates/art-20045705

Czeisler CA; Dumont M, Duffy JF; Steinberg JD, Richardson GS, Brown EN; Sánchez R, Ríos CD, Ronda JM, (n.d.). Association of sleep-wake habits in older people with changes in output of circadian pacemaker. Retrieved February 21, 2021, from https://pubmed.ncbi.nlm.nih.gov/1357348/

Federal Statistical Office. (2017, July 27). Hours worked increased in 2016 - Swiss labour FORCE survey and its derivative STATISTICS: Working hours: Press release. Retrieved February 21, 2021, from https://www.bfs.admin.ch/bfs/en/home/statistics/work-income/employment-working-hours/working-time.asset-detail.2967261.html

Friedman, L. (2014, February 07). 25 horrible things that happen if you don't get enough sleep. Retrieved February 21, 2021, from https://www.businessinsider.com/what-happens-if-you-dont-get-enough-sleep-2014-2?r=UK

Geniya. (n.d.). Sleep. Retrieved February 21, 2021, from https://resiliencei.com/sleep/

The global pursuit of better sleep health. (n.d.). Retrieved February 21, 2021, from https://www.usa.philips.com/

Greenwood, V., & Quanta Magazine moderates comments to facilitate an informed, S. (n.d.). Why sleep deprivation kills. Retrieved February 21, 2021, from https://www.quantamagazine.org/why-sleep-deprivation-kills-20200604/

Hayes, K. (2018, February 12). How much protein do you need after 50? Retrieved February 21, 2021, from https://www.aarp.org/health/healthy-living/info-2018/protein-needs-fd.html

Health benefits of a Mediterranean diet. Retrieved February 21, 2021, from https://www.health.com/nutrition/health-benefits-mediterranean-diet

Healthy diet. (n.d.). Retrieved February 21, 2021, from https://www.who.int/news-room/fact-sheets/detail/healthy-diet

Horan, L. (2019, November 15). This data shows a shocking worldwide lack of sleep. Retrieved February 21, 2021, from https://www.dreams.co.uk/sleep-matters-club/data-shows-a-shocking-worldwide-lack-of-sleep/

How to get your daily 30g of fibre. (2019, January 10). Retrieved February 21, 2021, from https://www.theguardian.com/society/2019/jan/10/how-to-get-your-daily-30g-of-fibre?

Kelland, K. (2011, September 18). Chronic disease to COST $47 trillion by 2030: WEF. Retrieved February 21, 2021, from https://www.reuters.com/article/us-disease-chronic-costs/chronic-disease-to-cost-47-trillion-by-2030-wef

Kernisan, L., Says, B., Says, S., Says, R., Says, G., Didyk, N., Says, P. (2020, August 28). 5 top causes of sleep problems in Aging, & proven ways to treat insomnia. Retrieved February 21, 2021, from https://betterhealthwhileaging.net/top-5-causes-sleep-problems-in-aging-and-proven-insomnia-treatments/

Kernisan, L., Says, J., Says, H., Says, B., Says, C., Says, A., Says, R. (2019, October 21). How sleep affects health, and changes with aging. Retrieved February 21, 2021, from https://betterhealthwhileaging.net/how-sleep-affects-health-and-changes-with-aging/

Kernisan, L., Says, S., Says, V., Says, O., Says, B., Benskin, L., Didyk, N. (2017, February 06). How to follow the Mediterranean diet for senior health. Retrieved February 21, 2021, from https://betterhealthwhileaging.net/how-to-follow-mediterranean-diet-for-senior-health/

Kohll, A. (2019, July 17). Nutrition: The missing piece of the corporate wellness puzzle. Retrieved February 21, 2021, from https://www.forbes.com/sites/alankohll/2019/07/17/nutrition-the-missing-piece-of-the-corporate-wellness-puzzle/#ad076d3f5014

Leah Groth Updated February 18, & Groth, L. (n.d.). The Mediterranean diet may help you avoid becoming frail in old Age, says new study. Retrieved February 21, 2021, from https://www.health.com

May, M. (2013). *Eat what you love, love what you eat: A mindful eating program to break your eat-repent-repeat cycle.* Am I Hungry? Publishing.

Mediterranean diet: Facts, benefits, and tips. (n.d.). Retrieved February 21, 2021, from https://www.medicalnewstoday.com/articles/149090#guidelines

Melinda. (n.d.). Sleep tips for older adults. Retrieved February 21, 2021, from https://www.helpguide.org/articles/sleep/how-to-sleep-well-as-you-age.htm

Obesity and overweight. (n.d.). Retrieved February 21, 2021, from https://www.who.int/news-room/fact-sheets/detail/obesity-and-overweight

O'Connor, A. (2016, January 07). Rethinking weight loss and the reasons we're 'always hungry'. Retrieved February 21, 2021, from https://well.blogs.nytimes.com/2016/01/07/rethinking-weight-loss-and-the-reasons-were-always-hungry

Older adults. (n.d.). Retrieved February 21, 2021, from https://www.myplate.gov/life-stages/older-adults

Plate and the planet. (2021, February 04). Retrieved February 21, 2021, from https://www.hsph.harvard.edu/nutritionsource/sustainability/plate-and-planet/

PMC, E. (n.d.). Europe pmc. Retrieved February 21, 2021, from https://europepmc.org/articles/pmc5227979

Protein. (2020, October 19). Retrieved February 21, 2021, from https://www.hsph. harvard.edu/nutritionsource/what-should-you-eat/protein/

Publishing, H. (n.d.). The truth about fats: The good, the bad, and the in-between. Retrieved February 21, 2021, from https://www.health.harvard.edu/staying-healthy/the-truth-about-fats-bad-and-good

Rimm, E., & Ellison, R. (1995, June). Alcohol in the Mediterranean diet. Retrieved February 21, 2021, from https://www.ncbi.nlm.nih.gov/pubmed/7754991

Roman, B., Carta, L., Martínez-González, M., & Serra-Majem, L. (2008). Effectiveness of the Mediterranean diet in the elderly. Retrieved February 21, 2021, from https://www.ncbi.nlm.nih.gov/pubmed/18494169

Sleep cycle: Sleep Tracker, monitor & alarm clock. (2020, December 18). Retrieved February 21, 2021, from https://www.sleepcycle.com/

Switzerland. (n.d.). Retrieved February 21, 2021, from http://www.oecdbetterlifeindex.org/countries/switzerland/

Vegetables and fruits. (2019, May 22). Retrieved February 21, 2021, from https://www. hsph.harvard.edu/nutritionsource/what-should-you-eat/vegetables-and-fruits/

Viens, A. (n.d.). *Are you sleeping enough? This infographic shows how you compare to the rest of the world.* World Economic Forum. https://www.weforum.org/ agenda/2019/08/we-need-more-sleep.

Villareal, D., Al., E., Author Affiliations From the Division of Geriatrics and Nutritional Science (D.T.V., F. P. Polack and Others, L. R. Baden and Others, & Consortium, W. (2011, June 23). Weight loss, exercise, or both and physical function in obese older adults: Nejm. Retrieved February 21, 2021, from https://www.nejm.org/doi/full/10.1056/nejmoa1008234

Wadyka, S. (n.d.). How to prevent colon cancer. Retrieved February 21, 2021, from https://www.consumerreports.org/colon-cancer/how-to-prevent-colon-cancer/

Wadyka, S. (n.d.). The surprising anti-aging benefits of fiber. Retrieved February 21, 2021, from https://www.consumerreports.org/diet-nutrition/anti-aging-benefits-of-fiber/

Emotional

About Tara Meyer-Robson - Tara Meyer. (n.d.). Retrieved February 21, 2021, from http://www.tarameyerrobson.com/about-tara-meyer-robson

Ageing - ageism. (n.d.). Retrieved February 21, 2021, from https://www.who.int/ data/maternal-newborn-child-adolescent-ageing/ageing-data/ageing---ageism

Avenue, N. (2018, May 07). Why life gets better after 50. Retrieved February 21, 2021, from https://www.forbes.com/sites/nextavenue/2018/05/06/why-life-gets-better-after-50/#5a484df64dee

Case studies. (n.d.). Retrieved February 21, 2021, from https://www.ageing-better.org.uk/case-studies

Chamine, S. (2016). *Positive Intelligence: Why only 20% of teams and individuals achieve their true potential and how you can achieve yours*. Greenleaf Book Group Press.

Charles, S., & Carstensen, L. (2010). Social and emotional aging. Retrieved February 21, 2021, from https://www.ncbi.nlm.nih.gov/pmc/articles/PMC3950961/

Depression. (n.d.). Retrieved February 21, 2021, from https://www.who.int/news-room/fact-sheets/detail/depression

Diener, E., Sandvik, E., & Pavot, W. (2009). Happiness is the frequency, not the intensity, of positive versus negative affect. *Assessing Well-Being,* 213-231. doi:10.1007/978-90-481-2354-4_10

Dispenza, D. (2020, May 08). Are you old?: How your thinking impacts your age. Retrieved February 21, 2021, from https://blog.drjoedispenza.com/blog/health/are-you-old-how-your-thinking-impacts-your-age?hs_amp=true

Ebner, N., & Fischer, H. (2014, September 9). Emotion and aging: Evidence from brain and behavior. Retrieved February 21, 2021, from https://www.ncbi.nlm.nih.gov/pmc/articles/PMC4158975

Freedman, J. (2021, March 2). *What's the Difference Between Emotion, Feeling, Mood?* Six Seconds. https://www.6seconds.org/2017/05/15/emotion-feeling-mood/.

How positive thinking builds skills, boosts health, and improves work. (2020, February 04). Retrieved February 21, 2021, from https://jamesclear.com/positive-thinking

How to stop negative self-talk. (2020, January 21). Retrieved February 21, 2021, from https://www.mayoclinic.org/healthy-lifestyle/stress-management/in-depth/positive-thinking/art-20043950

Hurley, K., Sood, A., Ellin, A., & Kilroy, D. (n.d.). What is resilience? Definition, types, building resiliency, benefits, and resources: Everyday health. Retrieved February 21, 2021, from https://www.everydayhealth.com/wellness/resilience/

Kals, E., & Maes, J. (2002). Sustainable development and emotions. *Psychology of Sustainable Development,* 97-122. doi:10.1007/978-1-4615-0995-0_6

Levy, B. R., Slade, M. D., Kunkel, S. R., & Kasl, S. V. (2002). Longevity increased by positive self-perceptions of aging. *Journal of Personality and Social Psychology, 83*(2), 261-270. doi:10.1037/0022-3514.83.2.261

Limbic system: Structure and function | emotion (video). (n.d.). Retrieved February 21, 2021, from https://www.khanacademy.org/science/health-and-medicine/executive-systems-of-the-brain/emotion-lesson/v/emotions-limbic-system

Logical positivism and logical empiricism. (n.d.). Retrieved February 21, 2021, from https://www.britannica.com/topic/positivism/Logical-positivism-and-logical-empiricism

The power of positive thinking. (n.d.). Retrieved February 21, 2021, from https://www.hopkinsmedicine.org/health/wellness-and-prevention/the-power-of-positive-thinking

Six Seconds supports people to create positive change - everywhere... all the time. Founded in 1997. (2020, December 02). White paper: Emotional Contagion • six seconds. Retrieved February 21, 2021, from https://www.6seconds.org/2004/04/17/white-paper-emotional-contagion/

Plutchik's wheel of emotions: Feelings WHEEL • six seconds. Retrieved February 21, 2021, from https://www.6seconds.org/2017/04/27/plutchiks-model-of-emotions/

The Swiss watch industry today. (n.d.). Retrieved February 21, 2021, from https://www.fhs.swiss/eng/watchindustrytoday.html

TBH toolkits. (n.d.). Retrieved February 21, 2021, from https://totalbrainhealth.com/

Today Show. (2006, January 26). Does your heart sense your emotional state? Retrieved February 21, 2021, from https://www.today.com/health/does-your-heart-sense-your-emotional-state-2D80555354

Verdolag, G. V. (2020, January 13). *The Real Meaning of Passion*. Embrace Possibility. https://www.embracepossibility.com/blog/real-meaning-passion/.

Why passion is so critically important to happiness. (n.d.). Retrieved February 21, 2021, from https://gretchenrubin.com/2007/04/why_passion_is

Young, A. (1999, January 01). Markets in time: The rise, fall, and revival of SWISS watchmaking: Anthony Young. Retrieved February 21, 2021, from https://fee.org/articles/markets-in-time-the-rise-fall-and-revival-of-swiss-watchmaking/

Intellectual

30 surprising facts about Switzerland: EXPATICA guide to Switzerland. (2021, February 08). Retrieved February 22, 2021, from https://www.expatica.com/ch/moving/about/switzerland-facts-100041/

Admin. (2018, August 14). The importance of play for Adults: Elder Options: North Central Florida. Retrieved February 22, 2021, from https://agingresources.org/the-importance-of-play-for-adults/

Bavishi, A., Slade, M., & Levy, B. (2016, July 18). A chapter a day: Association of book reading with longevity. Retrieved February 22, 2021, from https://www.sciencedirect.com/science/article/abs/pii/S0277953616303689

The Brain and Social Connectedness: GCBH Recommendations on Social Engagement and Brain Health (Rep.). (n.d.). Global council on Brain Health.

Cherry, K. (2019, December 07). What are fluid intelligence and crystallized intelligence? Retrieved February 22, 2021, from https://www.verywellmind.com/fluid-intelligence-vs-crystallized-intelligence-2795004

Clark, R., Freedberg, M., Hazeltine, E., & Voss, M. (n.d.). Are there age-related differences in the ability to learn configural responses? Retrieved February 22, 2021, from https://journals.plos.org/plosone/article?id=10.1371%2Fjournal.pone.0137260

Crooks, V., Lubben, J., Petitti, D., Little, D., & Chiu, V. (2008, July). Social network, cognitive function, and dementia incidence among elderly women. Retrieved February 22, 2021, from https://www.ncbi.nlm.nih.gov/pmc/articles/PMC2424087/

Dispenza, D. (n.d.). Creating the greatest ideal of yourself. Retrieved February 22, 2021, from https://blog.drjoedispenza.com/creating-the-greatest-ideal-of-yourself

Dispenza, D. (n.d.). The art of change. Retrieved February 22, 2021, from https://blog.drjoedispenza.com/the-art-of-change

Ecological intelligence. (n.d.). Retrieved February 22, 2021, from https://www.danielgoleman.info/books/ecological-intelligence/

Exercises to improve memory and concentration. (2021, February 19). Retrieved February 22, 2021, from https://neverleavetheplayground.com/

Global innovation INDEX 2020 — Switzerland remains the most innovative country in the world. (n.d.). Retrieved February 22, 2021, from https://www.ige.ch/en/services/newsroom/news/news-details/news/3755-global-innovation-index-2020-die-schweiz-bleibt-das-innovativste-land.html

Healthy aging is reflected in well-being, participation, playfulness, and cognitive-emotional functioning. (2015). *Healthy Aging Research.* doi:10.12715/har.2015.4.8

Margarita Tartakovsky, M. (2012, November 15). The importance of play for adults. Retrieved February 22, 2021, from https://psychcentral.com/blog/the-importance-of-play-for-adults/

Martínez-Alcalá, C., Rosales-Lagarde, A., Alonso-Lavernia, M., Ramírez-Salvador, J., Jiménez-Rodríguez, B., Cepeda-Rebollar, R., . . . Agis-Juárez, R. (2018, July 26). Digital inclusion in older adults: A comparison between face-to-face and blended digital literacy workshops. Retrieved February 22, 2021, from https://www.frontiersin.org/articles/10.3389/fict.2018.00021/full

Martínez-Alcalá, C., Rosales-Lagarde, A., Alonso-Lavernia, M., Ramírez-Salvador, J., Jiménez-Rodríguez, B., Cepeda-Rebollar, R., . . . Agis-Juárez, R. (2018, July 26). Digital inclusion in older adults: A comparison between face-to-face and blended digital literacy workshops. Retrieved February 22, 2021, from https://www.frontiersin.org/articles/10.3389/fict.2018.00021/full#B20

National Research Council (US) Committee on Aging Frontiers in Social Psychology, Personality, & Psychology, A. (1970, January 01). Motivation and behavioral change. Retrieved February 22, 2021, from https://www.ncbi.nlm.nih.gov/books/NBK83771/

Picture perfect playgrounds, inc. (n.d.). Retrieved February 22, 2021, from https://www.pgpedia.com/n/national-institute-play

Publishing, H. (n.d.). 12 ways to keep your brain young. Retrieved February 22, 2021, from https://www.health.harvard.edu/mind-and-mood/12-ways-to-keep-your-brain-young

Robinson, L. (n.d.). The benefits of play for adults. Retrieved February 22, 2021, from https://www.helpguide.org/articles/mental-health/benefits-of-play-for-adults.htm

Solan, M. (2019, March 28). The secret to happiness? Here's some advice from the longest-running study on happiness. Retrieved February 22, 2021, from https://www.health.harvard.edu/blog/the-secret-to-happiness-heres-some-advice-from-the-longest-running-study-on-happiness-2017100512543

Stanborough, R. (2019, October 15). Benefits of reading books: For your physical and mental health. Retrieved February 22, 2021, from https://www.healthline.com/health/benefits-of-reading-books#strengthens-the-brain

Vidovićová, L. New Roles for Older People. *Population Ageing* 11, 1–6 (2018). https://doi.org/10.1007/s12062-017-9217-z

Yarnal, C., & Qian, X. (n.d.). Older-Adult Playfulness An Innovative Construct and Measurement for Healthy Aging Research. Retrieved February 22, 2021, from https://psycnet.apa.org/record/2014-22135-002

Zimmermann@stlouisfed.org, & Lucia Ovidia Vreja & Sergiu Balan. (1970, January 01). Types of INTELLIGENCE. the ECOLOGICAL intelligence and Sustainability, by Lucia OVIDIA Vreja; Sergiu Balan. Retrieved February 22, 2021, from https://ideas.repec.org/a/aes/icafee/v7y2018p55-64.html

Spiritual

34 life-altering yoga statistics & facts for a balanced 2021. (2020, December 28). Retrieved February 22, 2021, from https://medalerthelp.org/yoga-statistics/

5 health benefits of daily Meditation according to science. (2021, February 17). Retrieved February 22, 2021, from https://positivepsychology.com/benefits-of-meditation/

AWAKE the film: Life of Paramahansa Yogananda (2020, October 30). Retrieved February 22, 2021, from http://consciouslivingtv.com/bianca-alexander/awake-the-film-life-of-paramahansa-yogananda.html

Clark, B. (2019, September 16). How to Breathe well as you age. Retrieved February 22, 2021, from https://yogainternational.com/article/view/how-to-breathe-well-as-you-age

Dispenza, D. (n.d.). Demystifying the meditation process. Retrieved February 22, 2021, from https://blog.drjoedispenza.com/blog/meditation/demystifying-the-meditation-process

Fountain-Zaragoza, S., & Prakash, R. (2017, February 3). Mindfulness training for healthy aging: Impact on attention, well-being, and inflammation. Retrieved February 22, 2021, from https://www.ncbi.nlm.nih.gov/pmc/articles/PMC5289973/

The Good Body. (2021, February 12). 24 meditation STATISTICS: Data and TRENDS revealed for 2021. Retrieved February 22, 2021, from https://www.thegoodbody.com/meditation-statistics/

Lu, Y., Rosner, B., Chang, G., & Fishman, L. (2016, April). Twelve-Minute daily YOGA regimen REVERSES Osteoporotic bone loss. Retrieved February 22, 2021, from https://www.ncbi.nlm.nih.gov/pmc/articles/PMC4851231/

Malone, J., & Dadswell, A. (2018, June 8). The role of Religion, Spirituality and/or belief in Positive ageing for older adults. Retrieved February 22, 2021, from https://www.ncbi.nlm.nih.gov/pmc/articles/PMC6319229/

Me, myself and yoga. (n.d.). Retrieved February 22, 2021, from https://www.nytimes.com/roomfordebate/2012/01/12/is-yoga-for-narcissists/the-purpose-of-yoga#:~:text=The%20original%20context%20of%20yoga,higher%20consciousness%20in%20the%20individual.

Peters, J., Grokker, Kiesling, S., & Foundation, S. (n.d.). Understanding the true purpose of yoga. Retrieved February 22, 2021, from https://spirituality-health.com/blogs/conscious-living/2017/07/20/understanding-the-true-purpose-of-yoga

Publishing, H. (n.d.). Giving thanks can make you happier. Retrieved February 22, 2021, from https://www.health.harvard.edu/healthbeat/giving-thanks-can-make-you-happier

Rachel. (2018, June 12). Difference between values and beliefs. Retrieved February 22, 2021, from http://www.differencebetween.net/language/difference-between-values-and-beliefs/

Rakicevic, M. (2021, January 13). 27 meditation statistics for your well-being in 2021. Retrieved February 22, 2021, from https://disturbmenot.co/meditation-statistics

Religion and spirituality in older people. (2020, March 11). Retrieved February 22, 2021, from https://www.seniorsmatter.com/religion-spirituality-older-people/2492159

Romero, L. (2017, November 27). Gratitude: The ultimate spiritual practice (a thanksgiving special). Retrieved February 22, 2021, from https://www.forbes.com/sites/luisromero/2017/11/22/gratitude-the-ultimate-spiritual-practice-a-thanksgiving-special/#485678832706

Sathyanarayana Rao, T., Asha, M., Jagannatha Rao, K., & Vasudevaraju, P. (2009). The biochemistry of belief. Retrieved February 22, 2021, from https://www.ncbi.nlm.nih.gov/pmc/articles/PMC2802367

Spiritual ecology. (2021, January 15). Retrieved February 22, 2021, from https://en.wikipedia.org/wiki/Spiritual_ecology

Spirituality. (n.d.). Retrieved February 22, 2021, from https://www.psychologytoday.com/us/basics/spirituality

Spirituality: Definition of spirituality by Oxford dictionary on LEXICO.COM also meaning of spirituality. (n.d.). Retrieved February 22, 2021, from https://www.lexico.com/definition/spirituality

Wei, M. (2017, July 14). Yoga can slow effects of stress and aging, studies suggest. Retrieved February 22, 2021, from https://www.psychologytoday.com/us/blog/urban-survival/201707/yoga-can-slow-effects-stress-and-aging-studies-suggest

Zuckerman, W. (2021, February 12). Significant yoga statistics: 2020/2021 benefits, facts & trends. Retrieved February 22, 2021, from https://comparecamp.com/yoga-statistics/

Financial

2020 Global Retirement Index An in-depth assessment of welfare in retirement around the world. (2020). Retrieved from https://investrends.ch/site/assets/files/27652/natixis_gri_2020.pdf

Charlton, E. S. (n.d.). *These are the most expensive cities to live in around the world*. World Economic Forum. https://www.weforum.org/agenda/2020/11/world-most-expensive-cities-covid-paris-zurich-singapore.

Department, P., & 23, N. (2020, November 23). Savings rate of households by Country 2019. Retrieved February 21, 2021, from https://www.statista.com/statistics/246296/savings-rate-in-percent-of-disposable-income-worldwide/

Dorsainvil, R. (2021, January 07). Why we can't talk about money without talking about culture. Retrieved February 21, 2021, from https://www.forbes.com/sites/riankadorsainvil/2019/06/28/why-we-cant-talk-about-money-without-talking-about-culture/?sh=25aabeaf5e8d

Garfield, L. (2015, December 17). The 10 best countries to live in around the world. Retrieved February 22, 2021, from https://www.businessinsider.com/the-top-countries-to-live-in-2015-12?r=UK#3-switzerland--people-in-switzerland-enjoy-low-cost-tuition-students-can-go-to-college-for-less-than-1000-per-semester-8

How to manage your money & be financially successful. (n.d.). Retrieved February 21, 2021, from https://www.annuity.org/financial-literacy/

Lusardi, A. (2019, January 24). *Financial literacy and the need for financial education: evidence and implications*. Swiss Journal of Economics and Statistics. https://sjes.springeropen.com/articles/10.1186/s41937-019-0027-5.

Money mindset: What is my relationship with money — and why? (n.d.). Retrieved February 21, 2021, from https://www.tomorrow.one/en-de/blog/money-mind-set-what-is-my-relationship-with-money-and-why

Nitch Smith, M. F. (n.d.). *You'll enjoy a high quality of life living in one of these countries*. World Economic Forum. https://www.weforum.org/agen-da/2018/01/how-s-life-where-you-are/.

Pettit, M., & *, N. (2020, June 02). How to increase happiness: 10 ways to be hap-py. Retrieved February 21, 2021, from https://lucemiconsulting.co.uk/in-crease-happiness/

Pettit, M., Mark Pettit on May 28, Mark Pettit on August 3, & *, N. (2020, August 24). 7 ways to develop an abundance mindset. Retrieved February 21, 2021, from https://lucemiconsulting.co.uk/abundance-mindset

Quiz: How do you relate to money? (n.d.). Retrieved February 21, 2021, from https://www.relate.org.uk/relationship-help/help-relationships/money/quiz-how-do-you-relate-money

R. Aggarwal, M., M. Argyle, A., I. Beutler, L., Boltanski, L., M. Brown, C., F. Bühl-mann, M., Zelizer, V. (1970, January 01). Culture, money attitudes and eco-nomic outcomes. Retrieved February 21, 2021, from https://sjes.springeropen.com/articles/10.1186/s41937-019-0028-4

Printed in Great Britain
by Amazon